Modern Biology

Active Reading Worksheets
with Answer Key

HOLT, RINEHART AND WINSTON

A Harcourt Education Company

Orlando • Austin • New York • San Diego • Toronto • London

To the Teacher

The Active Reading Worksheets help develop your students' reading skills as they review key concepts and illustrations. There is a worksheet for each section in each chapter of the Student Edition. Students will use comprehension, decoding, and vocabulary skills to identify relationships among words. Each reading passage contained in the guide relates to topics covered in the textbook. Completion of the worksheets serves to reinforce both students' reading skills and their understanding of core biology content. An introduction to the Active Reading Worksheets follows the Table of Contents. An Answer Key can be found at the back of this book.

Writer

Theresa Flynn-Nason
Science Teacher
Voorhees Public Schools
Voorhees, NJ

ISBN 0-03-036727-1

7 8 9   018   09 08 07

CONTENTS

Using the Active Reading Worksheets

Some students using *Modern Biology* may have an excellent knowledge and understanding of biology but may lack some reading skills that will allow them to compile and interpret information. The Active Reading Worksheets serves to develop and reinforce students' reading skills to make learning biology easier for students. Each worksheet contained in the guide correlates to a specific section of the *Modern Biology* Student Edition. The passages and illustrations that form the basis of each worksheet are related to topics in the textbook. Completion of the worksheets serves to reinforce students' reading skills and understanding of core biology content.

Reading Skills

There are many different types of printed matter, each of which has its own unique personality. As a result, the reading skills used to gain meaning from science texts generally differ from reading skills used to gain meaning from texts of other disciplines. The Active Reading Worksheets were designed to highlight the skills that facilitate understanding of science texts. Labels on each worksheet note the skill that is emphasized. The 10 reading skills are listed below.

- **Sequencing Information**   Science text commonly includes a description of a complex process broken down into a series of sequential steps. Recognition of this text structure is sparked by identification of clue words such as *first, prior, initially, then, before, after, next,* and *finally.* If readers approach a passage knowing it uses a sequential text structure, they are more likely to derive meaning from the text. An example from the worksheets is shown below.

Read the question and write your answers in the spaces provided.

SKILL: Sequencing Information

Order the statements to show the steps of a gene-transfer experiment. Write "1" on the line in front of the statement that describes what happens first. Write "2" on the line in front of the statement that describes what happens next, and so on.

_____ a. The plasmid is cut with restriction enzymes.

_____ b. As the bacterium divides, the donor gene is cloned.

_____ c. A donor gene is spliced into the plasmid.

_____ d. A plasmid is removed from a bacterium.

_____ e. The bacterium transfers the donor gene to other organisms it infects.

_____ f. The altered plasmid is returned to the bacterium.

- **Identifying Main Idea**   Every paragraph has a main idea (or topic sentence) and supporting details. Developing students' ability to identify the main idea and supporting details will not only aid students' comprehension of the text's key ideas but also serve to model writing strategies that they should use when responding to open-ended assessment questions.

- **Recognizing Similarities and Differences** Science text often introduces new concepts by comparing and contrasting new ideas with previously explored topics. Comparison key words, such as *like, similarly,* and *unlike,* and contrasting key words, such as *however, on the other hand,* and *differ* indicate this text structure. Graphic organizers, such as concept maps, flowcharts, and Venn diagrams, also focus the reader's attention on the similarities and differences between topics. Prior knowledge of these structures helps a reader gain meaning quickly and easily. An example from the worksheets is shown below.

Read each question and write your answer in the space provided.

SKILL: Recognizing Similarities and Differences

The diagram shows the two body forms of cnidarians. Complete the diagram by inserting the following labels: "Epidermis," "Gastrodermis," "Gastrovascular cavity," "Medusa," "Mesoglea," "Mouth," "Polyp," and "Tentacle."

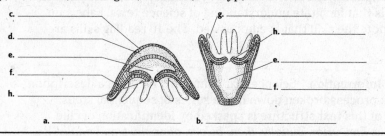

c. _____
d. _____
e. _____
f. _____
h. _____
a. _____
g. _____
h. _____
e. _____
f. _____
b. _____

- **Interpreting Graphics** A graphic is any type of visual that communicates information to an observer. The meaning a reader gains from a graphic depends on his or her recognition of its basic structures, such as the title, the labels, and the key. An example from the worksheets is shown below.

Observe the figure below and insert the correct label on the lines provided.

SKILL: Interpreting Graphics

The diagram below shows the structure of the female reproductive system. Write the following labels on the diagram: "Cervix," "Fallopian tube," "Labia," "Ovary," "Uterus," and "Vagina." Write your answers on the lines provided.

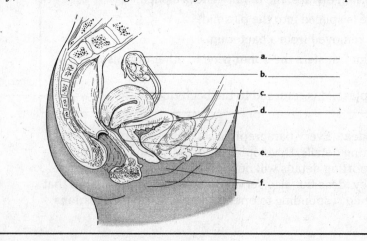

a. _____
b. _____
c. _____
d. _____
e. _____
f. _____

- **Organizing Information** Tables, charts, and graphic organizers are three devices commonly used to organize data. Realizing the significance of titles, headings, and symbols helps the reader recognize the structure of such organizers and gain meaning from them. An example from the worksheets is shown below.

Refer to the passage to complete the graphic organizer below.

SKILL: Organizing Information

Completing the graphic organizer will aid you in understanding the three different types of evolution.

Patterns of Evolution		
Evolution	**Pattern definition**	**Example**
1.	3.	parasites and their hosts
Convergent evolution	4.	5.
2.	two or more related species or populations become more and more dissimilar, often due to differing habitats	6.

- **Recognizing Text Structure** Text structure refers to the format an author uses to organize ideas and present a message in a logical manner. Patterns such as sequenced information, cause and effect, main idea and supporting details, and similarities and differences are four types of text structures often employed in science materials. By scanning a passage and identifying its text structure, a reader creates a scaffold for the organization of new ideas. As the reader goes back and actually reads the passage, he or she attaches the information to parts of the scaffold. This process facilitates the student's comprehension of the text.

- **Recognizing Cause and Effect** Another text structure used to convey scientific information is cause and effect. A cause-and-effect relationship defines how two seemingly isolated events are linked. The first event to occur, or the cause, causes a second event, or the effect. Skilled readers understand that certain clue words, such as *since, because,* and *due to,* generally precede a cause. Readers also recognize that other clue words, such as *consequently, as a result,* and *therefore,* often precede an effect. An example from the worksheets is shown on the next page.

Read each question and write your answer in the space provided.

SKILL: Recognizing Cause and Effect

One type of reading skill is the ability to recognize cause-and-effect relationships. In a cause-and-effect relationship, the cause is what makes something happen. The effect is the result of something and can be an event, decision, or situation.

1. What causes bryophytes to be small?

_____

2. What effect of mosses' ability to accumulate matter on the surface of rocks is described in the passage?

_____

_____

• **Completing Sentences**   Completing sentences, or the logical completion of an unfinished thought, can be used to reinforce any of the text structures noted above. Such exercises serve to develop understanding of relationships between words or ideas and serve as a model of effective writing strategies. An example from the worksheets appears below.

Complete the sentence by logically finishing the thought.

SKILL: Completing Sentences

1. The process by which bacteria in soil oxidize ammonia to form nitrates and nitrites is known as _____.

2. Denitrification occurs when _____ break down nitrates and release nitrogen gas back into the atmosphere.

3. Nitrogen fixation is the process of converting _____ to ammonia.

4. The organisms that convert nitrogen gas to ammonia are known as _____

_____.

5. The nitrogen cycle is the pathway that nitrogen flows within a(n) _____

_____.

• **Forming Analogies**   Analogies identify relationships between word pairs. Analogies can be used to develop word meanings, identify similarities and differences between items, note the parts of a whole, and reinforce understanding of an item and its function. An example from the worksheets is shown on the next page.

Write your answer in the space provided.

SKILL: Forming Analogies

An analogy identifies a similar relationship between different pairs of items. In an analogy, one must analyze the relationship between two words and then identify another pair of words that have the same relationship. In the analogy "The glove is to the hand as the sock is to the foot," the relationship is article of clothing to part of the body where worn.

1. Complete the following analogy: "Skin is to carcinoma as bone is to _____."

2. What relationship was used to form the analogy in question 1?
_____.

- **Vocabulary Development** Possible skills that fall under vocabulary development include recognizing words with multiple meanings, using context clues to define an unknown term, and using decoding skills to develop understanding of prefixes, suffixes, and base words. An example from the worksheets is shown below.

Write your answer in the space provided.

SKILL: Vocabulary Development

The prefix *uni-* means "one," while *multi-* means "many." The term *nucleate* means "having a nucleus." Use this information to define *uninucleate* and *multinucleate*.
_____
_____

Suggestions for Use

Each worksheet is a student-centered activity that can be completed independently. The flexible structure of the Active Reading Worksheets permits a wide array of uses in the classroom. Possible methods of use appear below.

- **Prereading Activity** Before beginning a section, distribute the corresponding worksheet to the students. Have them preview the section by reading through the worksheet questions. Then read the textbook section aloud as a whole group activity, and have students complete the worksheet as they come upon an answer. In this manner, previewing the section provides students with a motive for reading the section and helps direct their attention to certain key passages.

- **Postreading Activity** After reading a textbook section, distribute the corresponding worksheet to the students. Have them complete the worksheet independently, and then have them check answers with a partner or in a small group. In this manner, the worksheet acts as a tool for assessing understanding of the section's key ideas.

English-Language Learners/LEP Students

The guide can also be used to address the unique language needs of English-language learners and students with limited English proficiency. The following are specific suggestions for helping these students.

- Assessment scores often point out deficient skill areas of the test taker. If assessment records are available, scan the reading and language results of low-scoring readers, and note each student's problem areas. Correlate the test results with the reading skill labels found on each worksheet. Select corresponding worksheets to create a mini-workbook for each student that targets his or her individual weaknesses.

- In many districts, support staff such as ESL teachers, basic-skills teachers, and/or resource room teachers meet with low-scoring readers. Provide these instructors with the Active Reading Worksheets that correlate with a week's worth of classroom instruction. Support staff can use the work-sheets as the focus of parallel small-group instruction.

- Target a specific reading skill that needs to be reinforced. Select all of the Active Reading Worksheets worksheets that address this skill, and have students work through the worksheets in consecutive order. Because this method is not restricted to the location of content instruction, the method focuses on a specific reading skill rather than biology content.

Extension Activities

The following activities can be used to extend the reading skills developed in the guide.

- Direct students to a passage that uses a particular text structure, such as sequencing information. Challenge students to identify clue words that indicate this structure. Then have them complete a graphic organizer to show the steps of the process.

- Ask students to use a specific text structure to format their responses to an essay question.

- Have students create a graphic organizer that highlights the main idea and supporting details of a passage.

- Provide students with paper strips. Have them use the strips to create a physical model of a cause-and-effect text structure used in a passage. Have students label the first strip with the initial event described, or the cause. Have students label the next strip with the event that resulted, or the effect. This second event then acts as the cause of another event. When all strips have been labeled, have students attach the papers like links in a chain.

- Divide the class into small groups, and provide each group with 16 index cards. Have the students work cooperatively to find eight cause-and-effect relationships in a chapter. Have students label each of eight index cards with a cause and the remaining cards with an effect. Have groups swap cards, shuffle the cards, and place them face down on a table. Have one member of each group turn over two cards. If the cards display a cause and a subsequent effect, the student keeps the cards. If the cards do not match, they are returned to their original position. Group members take turns displaying cards. When all cards have been picked up, the student with the greatest number of cards is the winner.

- Identify a key prefix, such as *hydro-*. Have students scan the text to make a list of terms containing this prefix. Then have students define each entry on their list.

Name _____ Class _____ Date _____

THE SCIENCE OF LIFE

Section 1-1: The World of Biology

Read the passage below, which covers topics from your textbook. Answer the questions that follow.

All living things grow, as do many nonliving things. Nonliving things, such as crystals or icicles, grow by accumulating more of the material they are made of. Living things grow as a result of cell division and cell enlargement. **Cell division** is the formation of two cells from an existing cell. In unicellular organisms, cell division results in more organisms. Newly divided cells enlarge until they are the size of a mature cell. In multicellular organisms, however, organisms grow and mature through cell division, cell enlargement, and development.

Read the question and write your answer in the space provided.

SKILL: Identifying Main Ideas

One reading skill is the ability to identify the main idea of a passage. The main idea is the main focus or key idea. Frequently a main idea is accompanied by supporting information that offers detailed facts about the main idea.

1. What is the main idea of the passage?

_____

_____

Read the question and write your answer in the space provided.

SKILL: Vocabulary Development

2. The prefix *uni-* means "one," while *multi-* means "many." The term *nucleate* means "having a nucleus." Use this information to define *uninucleate* and *multinucleate*.

_____

_____

Circle the letter of the word or phrase that best completes the statement.

3. Growth occurs in multicellular organisms because of

    a. cell division.   **c.** development.

    b. cell enlargement.   **d.** All of the above

Name _____ Class _____ Date _____

THE SCIENCE OF LIFE

Section 1-2: Themes in Biology

Read the passage below, which covers topics from your textbook. Answer the questions that follow.

> [1]The **diversity,** or variety, of life, is amazing. [2]For example, there are single-celled organisms that thrive inside thick Antarctic ice that never thaws. [3]There are whales that contain about 1,000 trillion cells that can easily cruise the Pacific and migrate each year from Alaska to Mexico. [4]There are even plants that can capture and eat insects. [5]Biologists have identified more than 1.5 million species on Earth. [6]And there may be many more species that remain to be identified.

Read each question and write your answer in the space provided.

SKILL: Identifying Main Ideas

One reading skill is the ability to identify the main idea of a passage. The main idea is the main focus or key idea. Frequently a main idea is accompanied by supporting information that offers detailed facts about the main idea.

1. What sentence identifies the main idea of this passage?

   _____

2. What is the purpose of Sentences 2, 3, and 4?

   _____

3. Which sentence offers the best support for the main idea?

   _____

Circle the letter of the phrase that best completes the statement.

4. Every species of living things on Earth

   a. has been discovered and identified.
   b. has not yet been discovered and identified.
   c. lives in the Pacific Ocean.
   d. migrates each year.

CHAPTER 1 ACTIVE READING WORKSHEETS

THE SCIENCE OF LIFE

Section 1-3: The Study of Biology

**Read the passage below, which covers topics from your textbook.
Answer the questions that follow.**

When scientists have made many observations and collected
existing data, they suggest a possible explanation for what they
have seen and recorded. This explanation, called a **hypothesis,** is
a statement that both explains their observations and data and can
be tested. Hypothesizing is a very important step in scientific investigations. A statement is testable if evidence can be collected
that either supports or disproves it. A hypothesis may be shown to
be wrong, but it can never be proved true beyond all doubt. It can
only be supported by evidence. At any time, new data might indicate that a previously accepted hypothesis does not hold true in all
instances. Scientists often must refine and revise their original hy-
potheses—or even discard them—as they uncover new evidence.

To test a hypothesis, scientists make a prediction that logically
follows from the hypothesis. A **prediction** is a statement made in
advance that states the results that will be obtained from testing a
hypothesis, if the hypothesis is true. A prediction most often takes
the form of an "if-then" statement. A hypothesis is often tested by
carrying out an **experiment.** Experimenting is the process of testing a hypothesis and its predictions by gathering data under controlled conditions.

Read each question and write your answer in the space provided.

SKILL: Vocabulary Development

1. What key vocabulary terms are contained in this passage?

_____

2. Give the meaning of these terms.

_____

_____

continued on the next page . . .

Match each phase of the scientific method with the statement that describes it. In the space provided, write the letter corresponding to the correct phase.

    a. experiment
    b. hypothesis
    c. prediction

3. _____ often an "if-then" statement

4. _____ possible explanation for observations and data

5. _____ conducted under controlled conditions

6. _____ can be tested

7. _____ states what will likely occur through testing

8. _____ can never be proven true beyond all doubt

9. _____ tests the other two phases

10. _____ often revised as new evidence is gathered

SKILL: Sequencing Information

One reading skill is the ability to sequence information, or to logically place items or events in the order in which they occur.

11. Sequence the statements below to show the steps in the process used in scientific investigations. Write "1" on the line in front of the first step, "2" on the line in front of the second step, and so on.

    _____ **a.** Make a prediction.

    _____ **b.** Carry out an experiment.

    _____ **c.** Make observations and collect existing data.

    _____ **d.** Adjust or accept the hypothesis.

    _____ **e.** Form a hypothesis.

Circle the letter of the phrase that best completes the statement.

12. A hypothesis currently held to be true

    a. has been supported by experimentation.
    b. may be revised or discarded in the future.
    c. will never change.
    d. Both (a) and (b)

THE SCIENCE OF LIFE

Section 1-4: Tools and Techniques

**Read the passage below, which covers topics from your textbook.
Answer the questions that follow.**

Scientists use a single, standard system of measurement. The official name of the measurement system is Système International d'Unités (International System of Units), or simply SI. There are seven fundamental **base units** in SI that describe length, mass, time, and other quantities as shown in the table.

SI Base Units		
Base quantity	**Name**	**Abbreviation**
Length	meter	m
Mass	kilogram	kg
Time	second	s
Electric current	ampere	A
Thermodynamic temperature	kelvin	K
Amount of substance	mole	mol
Luminous (light) intensity	candela	cd

Read each question and write your answer in the space provided.

SKILL: Interpreting Graphics

One reading skill is the ability to interpret information, which means the ability to use or interpret tables and graphic organizers.

1. What is the title of the table?

   _____

2. How many rows and columns are there in the table?

   _____

continued on the next page . . .

SKILL: Forming Analogies

Another reading skill is the ability to recognize analogies. In an analogy, one must analyze the relationship between two words and then identify another pair of words that have the same relationship. Common phrases and words used in analogies are . . . *is to* . . . *as* (or *just as*) . . . *is to* . . . An example is "finger is to hand as toe is to foot," where the common relationship of the word pairs is digit to body structure where found.

3. What relationship was used to form the analogy "Meter is to m as kilogram is to kg"?

_____

_____

4. What relationship was used to form the analogy "Time is to second as electric current is to ampere"?

_____

Read the question and write your answer in the space provided.

SKILL: Vocabulary Development

5. The prefix *thermo-* comes from a Greek term meaning "heat." What would you expect to read about in a book on *thermochemistry*?

_____

Circle the letter of the word that best completes the analogy.

6. Electric current is to ampere as thermodynamic temperature is to

   a. K.
   b. A.
   c. kelvin.
   d. mole.

Name _____ Class _____ Date _____

CHEMISTRY OF LIFE

Section 2-1: Composition of Matter

Read the passage below, which covers topics from your textbook. Answer the questions that follow.

The central core, or **nucleus,** of an atom consists of two kinds of particles. One, the **proton,** has a positive electrical charge. The other, the **neutron,** has no electrical charge.

All atoms of a given element have the same number of protons. The number of protons in an atom is called the **atomic number** of the element.

In an atom, the number of positively charged protons is balanced by an equal number of small, negatively charged particles called **electrons.** The electrical charges of the electrons offset those of the protons, making the net electrical charge of an atom zero. Electrons are high-energy particles with very little mass. They move about the nucleus at very high speeds in one of several different orbitals. Electrons in outer orbitals have more energy than those in orbitals that are closer to the nucleus.

Write "P" on the line if the statement describes protons. Write "N" on the line if the statement describes neutrons. Write "E" on the line if the statement describes electrons.

SKILL: Vocabulary Development

1. _____ The atomic number indicates how many of these an atom contains.

2. _____ These high-energy particles have little mass.

3. _____ These lack an electrical charge.

4. _____ These are located in the nucleus of an atom.

5. _____ These have a positive electrical charge.

Circle the letter of the phrase that best completes the statement.

6. The net electrical charge of an atom is zero because it contains
   a. equal numbers of protons and electrons.
   b. more electrons than neutrons.
   c. fewer protons than electrons.
   d. equal numbers of neutrons and electrons.

CHAPTER 2 ACTIVE READING WORKSHEETS

CHEMISTRY OF LIFE

Section 2-2: Energy

Read the passage below, which covers topics from your textbook. Answer the questions that follow.

Many of the chemical reactions that help transfer energy in living things involve the transfer of electrons. These reactions in which electrons are transferred between atoms are known as oxidation-reduction reactions, or **redox reactions**. In an **oxidation** reaction, a reactant loses one or more electrons, thus becoming more positive in charge. In a **reduction** reaction, a reactant gains one or more electrons, thus becoming more negative in charge. Redox reactions always occur together. An oxidation reaction occurs, and the electron given up by one substance is then accepted by another substance in a reduction reaction.

Read each question and write your answer in the space provided.

SKILL: Recognizing Similarities and Differences

One reading skill is the ability to recognize similarities and differences between two phrases, ideas, or things. This skill is sometimes known as comparing and contrasting.

1. What is an oxidation reaction?

_____

_____

2. What is a reduction reaction?

_____

_____

Circle the letter of the phrase that best completes the statement.

3. Redox reactions transfer

   a. protons between living things.
   b. energy between living things.
   c. electrical charges between parts of an atom.
   d. Both (a) and (b)

CHAPTER 2 ACTIVE READING WORKSHEETS

CHEMISTRY OF LIFE

Section 2-3: Water and Solutions

Read the passage below, which covers topics from your textbook. Answer the questions that follow.

[1] A **solution** is a mixture in which one or more substances are uniformly distributed in another substance. [2] Solutions can be mixtures of liquids, solids, or gases. [3] A **solute** is the substance dissolved in the solution. [4] The **solvent** is the substance in which the solute is dissolved. [5] For example, when sugar, a solute, and water, a solvent, are mixed, a solution of sugar water results. [6] Though the sugar dissolves in the water, neither the sugar molecules nor the water molecules are altered chemically.

[7] Solutions can be composed of various proportions of a given solute in a given solvent. [8] Thus, solutions can vary in concentration. [9] The **concentration** of a solution is the measurement of the amount of solute dissolved in a fixed amount of solution. [10] For example, a 2 percent saltwater solution contains 2 g of salt dissolved in enough water to make 100 mL of solution. [11] The more solute dissolved, the greater the concentration of a solution. [12] A **saturated solution** is one in which no more solute can dissolve.

Read each question and write your answer in the space provided.

SKILL: Identifying Main Ideas

1. Which sentence identifies the main idea of the passage?

   _____

2. What supporting detail is provided in Sentence 2?

   _____

Circle the letter of the phrase that best completes the statement.

3. The greater the amount of solute dissolved in a solvent, the greater the

   a. number of ions in the solution.
   b. volume of the solution.
   c. number of charged molecules in the solution.
   d. concentration of the solution.

CHAPTER 3 ACTIVE READING WORKSHEETS

BIOCHEMISTRY

Section 3-1: Carbon Compounds

Read the passage below, which covers topics from your textbook. Answer the questions that follow.

An **alcohol** is an organic compound with a hydroxyl group attached to one of its carbon atoms. The hydroxyl group makes an alcohol a polar molecule. The alcohol ethanol causes cell death in the liver and brain of humans. The alcohol methanol, also called wood alcohol, can cause blindness or even death when consumed. Some alcohols, however, are needed by organisms to carry out their life processes. Humans, for example, need the alcohol glycerol to assemble certain molecules necessary for life.

Read each question and write your answer in the space provided.

SKILL: Recognizing Cause-and-Effect Relationships

One reading skill is the ability to recognize cause-and-effect relationships. In a cause-and-effect relationship, the cause is what makes something happen. The effect is the result of something and can be an event, decision, or situation.

1. What causes polarity in an alcohol?

_____

2. What effect does methanol have on the body?

_____

Read the question and write your answer in the space provided.

SKILL: Vocabulary Development

3. The prefix *hydro-* means "water." The suffix *-ate* means "having" or "characterized by." What, then, is a *hydrate*?

_____

Circle the letter of the term that answers the question.

4. Which alcohol is used by humans to assemble certain molecules necessary for life?

    a. ethanol   **c.** glycerol
    b. methanol   **d.** both (a) and (b)

CHAPTER 3 ACTIVE READING WORKSHEETS

BIOCHEMISTRY

Section 3-2: Molecules of Life

Read the passage below, which covers topics from your textbook. Answer the questions that follow.

Lipids are divided into categories according to their structure. Three classes of lipids important to living things contain fatty acids: triglycerides, phospholipids, and waxes. A *triglyceride* is composed of three molecules of fatty acid joined to one molecule of the alcohol glycerol. Saturated triglycerides are composed of saturated fatty acids. They typically have high melting points and tend to be hard at room temperature. In contrast, unsaturated triglycerides are composed of unsaturated fatty acids and are usually soft or liquid at room temperature.

Phospholipids have two, rather than three, fatty acids joined to a molecule of glycerol. The cell membrane is composed of two layers of phospholipids, which are referred to as the *lipid bilayer*. The inability of lipids to dissolve in water allows the membrane to form a barrier between the inside and outside of the cell. This bilayer arrangement of molecules produces a stable and effective barrier for a cell.

A **wax** is a type of structural lipid. A wax molecule consists of a long fatty-acid chain joined to a long alcohol chain. Waxes are highly waterproof, and in plants, waxes form a protective coating. Waxes also form protective layers in animals.

Fill in the blank to complete each sentence.

SKILL: Completing Sentences

One reading skill is the ability to complete an incomplete sentence by logically determining what will complete the unfinished thought.

1. Lipids are divided into categories according to their _____.

2. The three classes of lipids are _____.

3. Saturated triglycerides are composed of _____.

4. At room temperature, unsaturated triglycerides are _____.

5. The two layers of phospholipids that form the cell membrane are called the _____.

6. Lipids cannot dissolve in _____.

7. The bilayer arrangement of molecules in a cell membrane gives the cell a _____.

8. Waxes form a protective coating on the outer surfaces of _____.

Write your answers in the spaces provided.

SKILL: **Vocabulary Development**

Write "T" on the line if the statement describes triglycerides. Write "P" on the line if the statement describes phospholipids. Write "W" on the line if the statement describes waxes.

9. _____ They consist of a long fatty-acid chain joined to a long alcohol chain.

10. _____ Two categories of these are saturated and unsaturated.

11. _____ They consist of two molecules of fatty acids joined by a molecule of glycerol.

12. _____ Two layers of these enclose a cell.

13. _____ They consist of three molecules of fatty acids joined to one molecule of glycerol.

14. _____ They form a protective layer in animals.

Read the question and write your answer in the space provided.

15. The prefix *lipo-* is derived from a Greek term meaning "fat." The suffix *-oid* means "resembling" or "having the appearance of." What can you infer about a substance that is described as being *lipoid*?

_____

_____

Circle the letter of the phrase that best completes the statement.

16. A main structural difference between the three categories of lipids is the number of

    a. fatty-acid molecules present.
    b. alcohol molecules present.
    c. oxygen molecules present.
    d. Both (a) and (b)

CELL STRUCTURE AND FUNCTION

Section 4-1: The History of Cell Biology

Read the passage below, which covers topics from your textbook. Answer the questions that follow.

The discovery of cells was made possible by the development of the microscope in the 17th century. In 1665, the English scientist Robert Hooke used a microscope to examine a thin slice of cork. Hooke described it as consisting of "a great many little boxes." These "little boxes" reminded him of the cubicles or "cells" in which monks lived, so he called them cells.

What Hooke had observed were actually the remains of dead plant cells. The first person to observe living cells was a Dutch trader, Anton van Leeuwenhoek. Although van Leeuwenhoek's microscope was rather simple, in 1673 it was powerful enough to enable him to view the world of microscopic organisms which had never before been seen.

About 150 years passed before scientists began to organize the observations begun by Hooke and van Leeuwenhoek into a unified theory known as the cell theory. This theory has three parts:

(1) All living things are composed of one or more cells.

(2) Cells are the basic units of structure and function in an organism.

(3) Cells come only from the reproduction of existing cells.

Read each question and write your answer in the space provided.

SKILL: Identifying Main Ideas

1. What caused scientists to discover the existence of cells?

_____

2. What are the small rooms that monks lived in called?

_____

3. What did Hooke observe in the cork slice?

_____

continued on the next page . . .

4. What discovery is van Leeuwenhoek noted for?

_____

5. What are the three parts of the cell theory?

_____

_____

_____

Read the passage below, which covers topics from your textbook. Answer the questions that follow.

Early evidence for the cell theory was provided by German scientists. In 1838, the botanist Matthias Schleiden concluded that all plants are composed of cells. A year later, the zoologist Theodor Schwann came to the same conclusion about animals. In 1855, Rudolf Virchow, a physician who had been studying how disease affects living things, reasoned that cells come only from other cells. Over the years, modern scientists have gathered much additional evidence that strongly supports the cell theory.

Use the two passages to complete the table below.

SKILL: Organizing Information

6. The figure below indicates events that lead up to the cell theory. Complete the table by filling in the blank spaces.

Date	Scientist	Discovery
1665	a.	observed the remains of dead plant cells
b.	Anton van Leeuwenhoek	c.
1838	Matthias Schleiden	d.
e.	f.	stated that all animals are made of cells
1855	g.	h.

Circle the letter of the phrase that best completes the sentence.

7. The cell theory was

    a. first identified in 1665.

    b. the end result of many scientific investigations.

    c. described by Rudolf Virchow.

    d. Both (a) and (b)

CHAPTER 4 ACTIVE READING WORKSHEETS

CELL STRUCTURE AND FUNCTION

Section 4-2: Introduction to Cells

Read the passage below, which covers topics from your textbook. Answer the questions that follow.

As organisms evolved, their cells became more specialized and eventually were unable to survive independently. Groups of cells took on specific roles within the organism. A group of similar cells and their products that carry out a specific function is called a **tissue.** Groups of tissues that perform a particular job in an organism are called **organs.** An **organ system** is a group of organs that accomplish related tasks. The stomach and liver are organs that are part of the digestive system. Finally, several organ systems combine to make up an organism.

Read each question and write your answer in the space provided.

SKILL: Forming Analogies

Another reading skill is the ability to recognize analogies. In an analogy, one must analyze the relationship between two words and then identify another pair of words that have the same relationship. Common words and phrases used in analogies are . . . *is to . . . as* (or *just as*) . . . *is to . . .* An example is "finger is to hand as toe is to foot," where the common relationship of the word pairs is digit to body structure where found.

1. Complete the following analogy: "Tissues are to cells as organ systems are to

_____."

2. What relationship was used to form the analogy in question 1?

_____

Circle the letter of the word or phrase that best completes the analogy.

3. Organ systems
   a. are made up of a group of organs that work together.
   b. interact together to carry out the processes of life.
   c. work independently from each other.
   d. Both (a) and (b)

CHAPTER 4 ACTIVE READING WORKSHEETS

CELL STRUCTURE AND FUNCTION

Section 4-3: Cell Organelles and Features

**Read the passage below, which covers topics from your textbook.
Answer the questions that follow.**

Most of the functions of a eukaryotic cell are controlled by the nucleus. The nucleus is filled with a jellylike liquid called the *nucleoplasm*, which holds the contents of the nucleus and is similar in function to a cell's cytoplasm. The nucleus houses and protects the cell's genetic information. The hereditary information that contains the instructions for the structure and function of the organism is coded in the organism's DNA, which is contained in the nucleus. When a cell is not dividing, the DNA exists in the form of long, thin structures called *chromatin*. When a cell is about to divide, the DNA condenses to form **chromosomes.** Chromosomes are structures in the nucleus made of DNA and protein.

The nucleus is surrounded by a double membrane called the **nuclear envelope.** The nuclear envelope is made up of two phospholipid bilayers. Covering the surface of the nuclear envelope are tiny, protein-lined holes, which are called *nuclear pores*. The nuclear pores provide passageways for materials to enter and leave the nucleus.

Read the question and write your answer in the space provided.

SKILL: Recognizing Similarities and Differences

1. How is a nuclear envelope similar to a cell membrane?

_____

_____

Read the question and write your answer in the space provided.

SKILL: Vocabulary Development

2. The term *nucleus* is derived from a Latin word meaning "kernel" or "nut." How is the term *nucleus* related to its Latin term of origin?

_____

_____

Circle the letter of the word or phrase that best completes the sentence.

3. The nucleus is filled with a jellylike liquid called the

   a. nuclear pore.   **c.** chromatin.

   b. nuclear envelope.   **d.** nucleoplasm.

Name _____ Class _____ Date _____

CELL STRUCTURE AND FUNCTION

Section 4-4: Unique Features of Plant Cells

Read the passage below, which covers topics from your textbook. Answer the questions that follow.

Chloroplasts use light energy to make carbohydrates from carbon dioxide and water. Each chloroplast contains a system of flattened, membranous sacs called **thylakoids.** Thylakoids contain the green pigment **chlorophyll,** the main molecule that absorbs light and captures light energy for the cell. Chloroplasts can be found not only in plant cells but also in a wide variety of eukaryotic algae, such as seaweed.

Chloroplast DNA is very similar to the DNA of certain photosynthetic bacteria. Plant cell chloroplasts can arise only by the division of preexisting chloroplasts. These facts may suggest that chloroplasts are descendants of ancient prokaryotic cells. Like mitochondria, chloroplasts are also thought to be the descendants of ancient prokaryotic cells that were incorporated into plant cells through a process called *endosymbiosis.*

Read the question and write your answer in the space provided.

SKILL: Recognizing Cause-and-Effect Relationships

1. How does a plant get the energy it needs to make carbohydrates?

_____

_____

2. How do scientists think chloroplasts evolved?

_____

_____

_____

CHAPTER 5 ACTIVE READING WORKSHEETS

HOMEOSTASIS AND CELL TRANSPORT

Section 5-1: Passive Transport

**Read the passage below, which covers topics from your textbook.
Answer the questions that follow.**

One type of passive transport is called **facilitated diffusion.** This process is used for molecules that cannot readily diffuse through cell membranes, even when there is a concentration gradient across the membrane. Such molecules may not be soluble in lipids, or they may be too large to pass through the pores in the membrane. In facilitated diffusion, the movement of these kinds of molecules across the cell membrane is assisted by specific proteins in the membrane. These proteins are known as **carrier proteins.**

In facilitated diffusion, a carrier protein binds to a specific molecule it transports. As soon as the molecule binds to the carrier protein, the carrier protein changes shape. This altered shape may shield the molecule from the hydrophobic interior of the lipid bilayer. Once shielded, the molecule can be transported across the cell membrane. On the other side of the membrane, the molecule is released from the carrier protein, which then returns to its original shape.

Read each question and write your answer in the space provided.

SKILL: Sequencing Information

1. Order the statements to show the steps of facilitated diffusion. Write "1" on the line in front of the statement that describes what happens first. Write "2" on the line in front of the statement that describes what happens next, and so on.

   a. _____ The molecule is released from the carrier protein.

   b. _____ The carrier protein changes shape.

   c. _____ The molecule is transported across the cell membrane.

   d. _____ The molecule binds to a carrier protein.

   e. _____ The carrier protein returns to its original shape.

   f. _____ The molecule is shielded from the hydrophobic interior of the lipid bilayer.

continued on the next page . . .

2. In order of occurrence, briefly describe what happens in each of the three main parts of facilitated diffusion.

a. _____

b. _____

_____

c. _____

Write your answer in the space provided.

SKILL: Vocabulary Development

3. The term *diffusion* comes from a Latin word meaning "to spread apart." How is the term *diffusion* related to its Latin word of origin?

_____

Circle the letter of the phrase that best answers the question.

4. What types of molecules diffuse through the cell membrane by facilitated diffusion?

a. molecules that are not soluble in lipids

b. molecules that are too large to pass through pores in the membrane

c. molecules that can survive the hydrophobic interior of the lipid bilayer

d. both (a) and (b)

Name _____ Class _____ Date _____

HOMEOSTASIS AND TRANSPORT

Section 5-2: Active Transport

Read the passage below, which covers topics from your textbook. Answer the questions that follow.

Endocytosis is the process by which cells ingest external fluid, macromolecules, and large particles, including other cells. These external materials are enclosed by a portion of the cell's membrane, which folds into itself and forms a pouch. The pouch then pinches off from the cell membrane and becomes a membrane-bound organelle called a **vesicle.** Some of the vesicles fuse with lysosomes, and their contents are digested by lysosomal enzymes. Other vesicles that form during endocytosis fuse with other membrane-bound organelles.

Exocytosis is essentially the reverse of endocytosis. During exocytosis, vesicles in the cytoplasm fuse with the cell membrane, releasing their contents into the cell's external environment. Cells can use exocytosis to release large molecules such as proteins, waste products, or toxins that would damage the cell if they were released within the cytosol. Proteins are made on ribosomes and packaged into vesicles by the Golgi apparatus. The vesicles then move to the cell membrane and fuse with it, delivering the proteins outside the cell.

Fill in the blank to complete each sentence.

SKILL: Completing Sentences

1. Endocytosis is the process by which cells ingest large particles, external fluid, and _____ .

2. During exocytosis, substances are released from the cell through a _____ .

3. Through exocytosis, a cell releases large molecules such as _____ .

Circle the letter of the phrase that best completes the statement.

4. Endocytosis and exocytosis are similar in that both processes involve the
   a. ingestion of substances.
   b. release of substances from a cell.
   c. movement of large particles across a cell membrane.
   d. Both (a) and (b)

CHAPTER 6 ACTIVE READING WORKSHEETS

PHOTOSYNTHESIS

Section 6-1: The Light Reactions

**Read the passage below, which covers topics from your textbook.
Answer the questions that follow.**

[1] Located in the membrane of the thylakoids are a variety of
pigments, the most important of which are called **chlorophylls.**
[2] There are several different types of chlorophylls. [3] The two
most common types are known as chlorophyll *a* and chlorophyll *b*.

[4] A slight difference in molecular structure between chlorophyll
a and chlorophyll *b* causes the two molecules to absorb different
colors of light. [5] Chlorophyll *a* absorbs less blue light but more red
light than chlorophyll *b* absorbs. [6] Neither chlorophyll *a* nor chlorophyll *b* absorbs much green light. [7] Instead, they allow green light to
be reflected or transmitted. [8] That is why leaves and other plant
structures that contain large amounts of chlorophyll look green.
[9] Only chlorophyll *a* is directly involved in the light reactions of
photosynthesis. [10] Chlorophyll *b* assists chlorophyll *a* in capturing
light energy; therefore, chlorophyll *b* is called an accessory pigment.

Read each question and write your answer in the space provided.

SKILL: Identifying Main Ideas

1. Which sentence identifies the main idea of the first paragraph?

   _____

2. What supporting details are described by the remaining sentences in the first paragraph?

   _____

   _____

Read the questions and write your answers in the spaces provided.

SKILL: Recognizing Similarities and Differences

**One reading skill is the ability to recognize similarities and differences between two
phrases, ideas, or things. This skill is sometimes known as comparing and contrasting.
Some clue words that writers use when pointing out similarities or making comparisons
are *like, as, similarly, similar to, neither, nor,* and *in the same way.* Some clue words that
writers use when pointing out differences or making contrasts include *however, but,
although, on the contrary, still, either, or,* and *on the other hand.*** *continued on the next page . . .*

3. What difference between chlorophyll *a* and chlorophyll *b* is noted in Sentence 4?

_____

_____

_____

4. Does Sentence 5 note a similarity or a difference between these molecules?

_____

5. What is the similarity or difference noted in Sentence 5?

_____

_____

6. Does Sentence 6 note a similarity or a difference?

_____

7. What is the similarity or difference noted in Sentence 6?

_____

_____

Read the question and write your answer in the space provided.

SKILL: **Recognizing Cause-and-Effect Relationships**

In a cause-and-effect relationship, one event, or cause, triggers a second event, or effect, to occur. Determine the cause or effect in the question below.

8. What is the effect of the difference between chlorophyll *a* and chlorophyll *b*?

_____

_____

Circle the letter of the phrase that best completes the statement.

9. Because chlorophyll *b* assists chlorophyll *a* in capturing light energy, chlorophyll *b*

    a. is a carotenoid.
    b. is called an accessory pigment.
    c. absorbs more blue light than chlorophyll *a*.
    d. reflects green light.

CHAPTER 6 ACTIVE READING WORKSHEETS

PHOTOSYNTHESIS

Section 6-2: The Calvin Cycle

Read the passage below, which covers topics from your textbook. Answer the questions that follow.

The Calvin cycle has four major steps that occur within the stroma of the chloroplasts.

Step 1. CO_2 diffuses into the stroma from the surrounding cytosol. An enzyme combines each CO_2 molecule with a five-carbon carbohydrate called RuBP. The product is a six-carbon molecule that splits immediately into a pair of three-carbon molecules known as 3-PGA.

Step 2. Each molecule of 3-PGA is converted into another three-carbon molecule, G3P, in a two-part process. First, each 3-PGA molecule receives a phosphate group from a molecule of ATP. The resulting compound then receives a proton from NADPH and releases a phosphate group, producing G3P. In addition to G3P, these reactions produce ADP, $NADP^+$, and phosphate. These three products can be used again in the light reactions to synthesize additional molecules of ATP and NADPH.

Step 3. One molecule of G3P is used to make organic compounds.

Step 4. Most of the G3P is converted back into RuBP in a complicated series of reactions. These reactions require a phosphate group from another molecule of ATP, which is changed into ADP. By regenerating the RuBP that was consumed in Step 1, the reactions of Step 4 allow the Calvin cycle to continue operating.

Read each question and write your answer in the space provided.

SKILL: Identifying Main Ideas

1. Summarize the main events that occur in each step of the Calvin cycle on the lines provided.

   a. Step 1

   _____

   _____

continued on the next page . . .

b. Step 2

_____

_____

c. Step 3

_____

_____

d. Step 4

_____

_____

Read the question and write your answer in the space provided.

SKILL: Vocabulary Development

2. The prefix *cyto-* means "cell." The suffix *-logy* means "study." How does knowledge of these word parts help define *cytology*?

_____

_____

_____

Circle the letter of the phrase that best completes the sentence.

3. If the RuBP consumed in Step 1 was not regenerated in Step 4 of the Calvin cycle, then

   a. CO_2 would stop diffusing into the stroma.

   b. the cycle would speed up because of an increase in CO_2 molecules.

   c. the plant cell would lack G3P molecules.

   d. the plant cell would stop bonding carbon atoms from CO_2 into organic compounds.

CHAPTER 7 ACTIVE READING WORKSHEETS

CELLULAR RESPIRATION

Section 7-1: Glycolysis and Fermentation

**Read the passage below, which covers topics from your textbook.
Answer the questions that follow.**

Glycolysis is a pathway in which one six-carbon molecule of glucose is oxidized to produce two three-carbon molecules of pyruvic acid. The pathway can be condensed into the following four main steps.

Step 1. Two phosphate groups are attached to one molecule of glucose, forming a new six-carbon compound. The phosphate groups are supplied by two molecules of ATP, which are converted into two molecules of ADP in the process.

Step 2. The six-carbon compound formed in Step 1 is split into two three-carbon molecules of glyceraldehyde 3 = phosphate (G3P).

Step 3. The two G3P molecules are oxidized, and each receives a phosphate group. The product of this step is two molecules of a new three-carbon compound. The oxidation of G3P is accompanied by the reduction of two molecules of NAD^+ to NADH. Like $NADP^+$, NAD^+ is an organic molecule that accepts electrons during redox reactions.

Step 4. The phosphate groups added in Step 1 and Step 3 are removed from the three-carbon compounds formed in Step 3. This reaction produces two molecules of pyruvic acid. Each phosphate group is combined with a molecule of ADP to make a molecule of ATP. Because a total of four phosphate groups were added in Step 1 and Step 3, four molecules of ATP are produced.

Read each question and write your answer in the space provided.

SKILL: Recognizing Text Structure

A writer will use different types of text structure to present organized ideas or events. The ability to understand how ideas are organized will help you understand a text. Some of the patterns of text structure you may have seen in earlier sections are compare and contrast (similarities and differences), cause and effect, and sequencing information.

1. What text structure is used to present this information to the reader?

_____

continued on the next page . . .

2. What is the final product of glycolysis?

_____

_____

3. Insert the following labels on the diagram to show the steps of glycolysis: "4 ATP," "2 ATP," "2 molecules of 3-carbon compound," "Glucose," "2 molecules of pyruvic acid," "6-carbon compound," and "2 molecules of G3P."

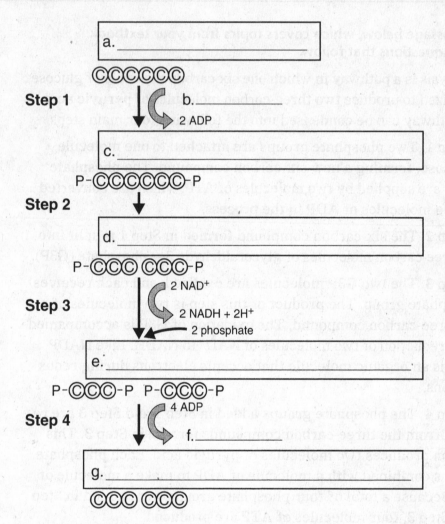

Circle the letter of the phrase that best completes the statement.

4. NADP$^+$ and NAD$^+$ are similar in that both

a. accept electrons during redox reactions.

b. are types of organic molecules.

c. are forms of pyruvic acid.

d. Both (a) and (b)

CHAPTER 7 ACTIVE READING WORKSHEETS

CELLULAR RESPIRATION

Section 7-2: Aerobic Respiration

Read the passage below, which covers topics from your textbook. Answer the questions that follow.

The Krebs cycle has five main steps. In eukaryotic cells, all five steps occur in the mitochondrial matrix.

Step 1. A two-carbon molecule of acetyl CoA combines with a four-carbon compound, **oxaloacetic acid,** to produce a six-carbon compound, **citric acid.**

Step 2. Citric acid releases a CO_2 molecule and a hydrogen atom to form a five-carbon compound. The electron in the hydrogen atom is transferred to NAD^+, reducing it to NADH.

Step 3. The five-carbon compound formed in Step 2 also releases a CO_2 molecule and a hydrogen atom, forming a four-carbon compound. Again, NAD^+ is reduced to NADH. In this step, a molecule of ATP is also synthesized from ADP.

Step 4. The four-carbon compound formed in Step 3 releases a hydrogen atom to form another four-carbon compound. This time, the hydrogen atom is used to reduce FAD to $FADH_2$. **FAD,** or flavin adenine dinucleotide, is a molecule very similar to NAD^+. Like NAD^+, FAD accepts electrons during redox reactions.

Step 5. The four-carbon compound formed in Step 4 releases a hydrogen atom to regenerate oxaloacetic acid, which keeps the Krebs cycle operating. The electron in the hydrogen atom reduces NAD^+ to NADH.

Recall that in glycolysis one glucose molecule produces two pyruvic acid molecules, which can then form two molecules of acetyl CoA. Thus, one glucose molecule is completely broken down in two turns of the Krebs cycle. These two turns produce six NADH, two $FADH_2$, two ATP, and four CO_2 molecules.

Write your answers in the spaces provided.

SKILL: Sequencing Information

1. Sequence the events to show the order in which they occur during the Krebs cycle. Write "1" on the line in front of the event that occurs first. Write "2" on the line in front of the event that occurs next, and so on.

continued on the next page . . .

_____ **a.** Citric acid releases a CO_2 molecule and a hydrogen atom to form a five-carbon compound.

_____ **b.** A four-carbon compound is converted into oxaloacetic acid.

_____ **c.** A five-carbon compound releases a CO_2 molecule to form a four-carbon compound.

_____ **d.** A molecule of acetyl CoA combines with oxaloacetic acid to produce citric acid.

_____ **e.** A four-carbon compound releases a hydrogen atom to form another four-carbon compound.

Write your answers in the spaces provided.

2. The figure below shows the Krebs cycle. Using the information contained in the passage, write the name of the compound at each lettered block on the lines below the figure. Use the following labels: "4-carbon compound," "5-carbon compound," "Oxaloacetic acid," and "Citric acid." You will use a label more than once.

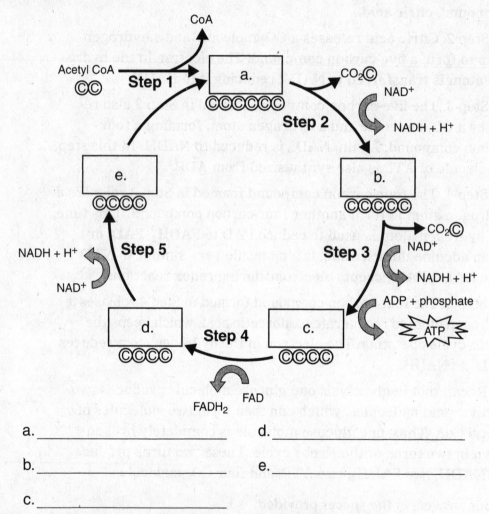

a._____   d._____

b._____   e._____

c._____

Circle the letter of the phrase that best completes the statement.

3. Two completions of the Krebs cycle produce six NADH, two $FADH_2$, four CO_2, and

   a. four glucose molecules.   **c.** four ATP molecules.
   b. two ATP molecules.   **d.** Both (a) and (b)

Name _____ Class _____ Date _____

CELL REPRODUCTION

Section 8-1: Chromosomes

Read the passage below, which covers topics from your textbook. Answer the questions that follow.

Human and animal chromosomes are categorized as either sex chromosomes or autosomes. **Sex chromosomes** are chromosomes that determine the sex of an organism, and they may also carry genes for other characteristics. In humans, sex chromosomes are either X or Y. Females normally have two X chromosomes, and males normally have an X and a Y chromosome. All of the other chromosomes in an organism are called **autosomes.** Two of the 46 human chromosomes are sex chromosomes, while the remaining 44 chromosomes are autosomes.

Every cell of an organism produced by sexual reproduction has two copies of each autosome. The organism receives one copy of each autosome from each parent. The two copies of each autosome are called **homologous chromosomes,** or homologues. Homologous chromosomes are the same size and shape and carry genes for the same traits.

Read each question and write your answer in the space provided.

SKILL: Recognizing Similarities and Differences

1. What are the similarities and differences of the sex chromosomes of a male and a female?

_____

_____

2. How are homologues alike?

_____

_____

Circle the letter of the word that best completes the analogy.

3. In humans, sex chromosomes are to 2 as autosomes are to

    a. 46.

    b. 22.

    c. 44.

    d. 18.

CHAPTER 8 ACTIVE READING WORKSHEETS

CELL REPRODUCTION

Section 8-2: Cell Division

Read the passage below, which covers topics from your textbook. Answer the questions that follow.

Mitosis is a continuous process that is divided into four phases: prophase, metaphase, anaphase, and telophase. **Prophase** is the first phase of mitosis. Prophase begins with the shortening and tight coiling of DNA into rod-shaped chromosomes that can be seen with a light microscope. During the S phase, each chromosome is copied. The two copies of each chromosome—called chromatids—stay connected to one another by the centromere. At this time, the nucleolus and the nuclear membrane break down and disappear. Two pairs of dark spots called *centrosomes* appear next to the disappearing nucleus. The centrosomes move toward opposite poles of the cell, and **spindle fibers** radiate from the centrosomes in preparation for mitosis.

Metaphase is the second phase of mitosis. During metaphase, kinetochore fibers move the chromosomes to the center of the dividing cell.

During **anaphase,** the chromatids of each chromosome separate at the centromere and slowly move toward opposite poles of the dividing cell. After the chromatids separate, they are considered to be individual chromosomes.

Telophase is the fourth phase of mitosis. After the chromosomes reach opposite ends of the cell, the spindle fibers disassemble and the chromosomes return to a less tightly coiled chromatin state. A nuclear envelope forms around each set of chromosomes, and a nucleolus forms in each of the newly forming cells.

Match each statement with the phase of mitosis it describes. Write the letter corresponding to the correct phase in the space provided.

SKILL: Sequencing Information

In this exercise, matching the statement with the stage of mitosis will help you learn the sequence of events of mitosis.

      a. prophase   **c.** anaphase

      b. metaphase   **d.** telophase

1. _____ Chromatids of each chromosome separate at the centromere.

2. _____ Copied DNA coils into chromosomes.

3. _____ Spindle fibers disassemble.

4. _____ Kinetochore fibers move chromosomes to the cell's center.

5. _____ Centrosomes appear next to the disappearing nucleus.

6. _____ A nucleolus forms in each newly formed cell.

7. _____ Chromatids move toward opposite poles of the dividing cell.

8. _____ Spindle fibers radiate from the centrosomes.

9. _____ A nuclear envelope forms around each set of chromosomes.

Write your answers in the spaces provided.

SKILL: Interpreting Graphics

10. The figure below shows the phases of mitosis. Using the information contained in the passage, write the name of the structure on each lettered line. On the numbered lines below the figure, name the stage of mitosis corresponding to the number on the figure. Use the following labels: "Anaphase," "Centromere," "Centrosomes," "Metaphase," "Nuclear envelope," "Prophase," "Spindle fibers," and "Telophase."

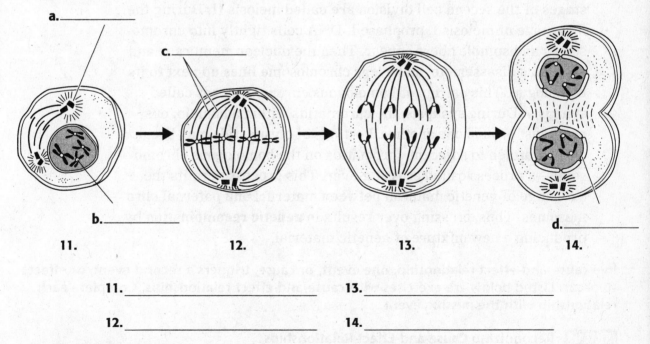

a._____

c._____

b._____   d._____

11.   12.   13.   14.

11._____ 13._____

12._____ 14._____

Circle the letter of the word or phrase that best completes the analogy.

15. Prophase is to centrosomes as telophase is to

    a. chromatids.
    b. nucleolus.
    c. kinetochore fibers.
    d. spindle fibers.

Name _____ Class _____ Date _____

CELL REPRODUCTION

Section 8-3: Meiosis

Read the passage below, which covers topics from your textbook. Answer the questions that follow.

Meiosis is a process of nuclear division that reduces the number of chromosomes in new cells to half the number in the original cell. In animals, meiosis produces haploid reproductive cells called gametes. Human gametes are sperm cells and egg cells, each of which contains 23 ($1n$) chromosomes. The fusion of a sperm and egg results in a zygote that contains 46 ($2n$) chromosomes. Cells begin meiosis with a duplicate set of chromosomes, just as cells beginning mitosis do. Because cells undergoing meiosis divide twice, diploid ($2n$) cells that divide meiotically result in four haploid cells ($1n$) rather than two diploid ($2n$) cells.

The stages of the first cell division are called meiosis I, and the stages of the second cell division are called meiosis II. During the first stage of meiosis I, prophase I, DNA coils tightly into chromosomes and spindle fibers appear. Then the nuclear membrane and nucleolus disassemble, and every chromosome lines up next to its homologue. This pairing of homologous chromosomes is called **synapsis.** During synapsis, the chromatids within a homologous pair twist around one another. Portions of chromatids may break off and attach to adjacent chromatids on the homologous chromosome—a process called **crossing-over.** This process permits the exchange of genetic material between maternal and paternal chromosomes. Thus, crossing-over results in **genetic recombination** by producing a new mixture of genetic material.

In a cause-and-effect relationship, one event, or cause, triggers a second event, or effect, to occur. Listed below are exercises with cause-and-effect relationships. Complete each relationship with the missing event.

SKILL: Recognizing Cause-and-Effect Relationships

1. Cause: <u>In humans, meiosis produces haploid reproductive cells called gametes.</u>

   Effect: _____

2. Cause: _____

   Effect: <u>A zygote contains 46 chromosomes.</u>

3. Cause: <u>During synapsis, chromatids within a homologous pair may twist around one another.</u>

Effect: _____

4. Cause: _____

Effect: <u>A new mixture of genetic material results in genetic recombination.</u>

Read the question and write your answer in the space provided.

SKILL: Vocabulary Development

5. The term *synapsis* comes from a Greek word meaning "point of contact." How is the term *synapsis* related to its Greek word of origin?

_____

_____

_____

Circle the letter of the phrase that best completes the statement.

6. During prophase I,

    a. DNA coils into chromosomes.
    b. spindle fibers appear.
    c. gametes fuse.
    d. Both (a) and (b)

CHAPTER 9 ACTIVE READING WORKSHEETS

FUNDAMENTALS OF GENETICS

Section 9-1: Mendel's Legacy

Read the passage below, which covers topics from your textbook. Answer the questions that follow.

Mendel concluded that paired factors separate during the formation of reproductive cells. This means that each reproductive cell, or gamete, receives only one factor of each pair. When two gametes combine during fertilization, the offspring have two factors controlling a specific trait. The **law of segregation** states that a pair of factors is segregated, or separated, during the formation of gametes.

Mendel also crossed plants that differed in two characteristics, such as flower color and seed color. The data from these more complex crosses showed that traits produced by dominant factors do not necessarily appear together. A green seed pod produced by a dominant factor could appear in a white-flowering pea plant. Mendel concluded that the factors for different characteristics are not connected. The **law of independent assortment** states that factors separate independently of one another during the formation of gametes.

Fill in the blank to complete each sentence.

SKILL: Completing Sentences

1. During the formation of reproductive cells, paired factors _____.

2. Because of this separation, each gamete receives only _____.

3. Offspring have two factors controlling a specific trait because gametes combine during _____.

4. The law of segregation states that _____.

5. Traits produced by dominant factors do not necessarily appear _____.

Circle the letter of the phrase that best completes the statement.

6. The fact that a green seed pod could appear in a white-flowering pea plant supports the

   a. law of segregation.
   b. law of independent assortment.
   c. theory of fertilization.
   d. Both (a) and (b)

FUNDAMENTALS OF GENETICS

Section 9-2: Genetic Crosses

Read the passage below, which covers topics from your textbook. Answer the questions that follow.

Biologists use a diagram called a **Punnett square** to aid them in predicting the probable distribution of inherited traits in the offspring.

In rabbits, the allele for black coat color (*B*) is dominant over the allele for brown coat color (*b*). The Punnett square below shows the predicted results of crossing two rabbits that are both heterozygous (*Bb*) for coat color. As you can see, 1/4 (25 percent) of the offspring are predicted to have the genotype *BB*, 1/2 (50 percent) are predicted to have the genotype *Bb*, and 1/4 (25 percent) are predicted to have the genotype *bb*. Thus, 3/4 (75 percent) of the offspring resulting from this cross are predicted to have a black coat. One-fourth (25 percent) of the offspring are predicted to have a brown coat. The ratio of the genotypes that appear in offspring is called the **genotypic ratio**. The ratio of the offspring's phenotypes is called the **phenotypic ratio**.

Read each question and write your answer in the space provided.

SKILL: Interpreting Graphics

1. The figure below is a Punnett square. Using the information provided in the passage and the figure, answer the questions that follow.

(Bb)

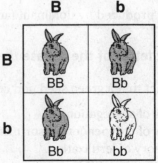

a. What is the purpose of this figure?

_____

b. The passage states that both parents are heterozygous for coat color. What does this statement mean?

_____

_____

c. How can you use the information in the figure to determine the coat color of the parents?

_____

_____

d. What are the genotypes of predicted homozygous offspring?

_____

_____

e. What is the probable genotypic ratio of the cross represented in the graphic?

_____

f. What is the probable phenotypic ratio of the cross represented in the graphic?

_____

Read the question and write your answer in the space provided.

SKILL: Vocabulary Development

2. The prefix *pheno-* is derived from a Greek term meaning "to show." How does knowledge of this word part aid in decoding the term *phenotype*?

_____

_____

_____

Circle the letter of the word or phrase that best completes the statement.

3. Another Punnett square yielded 2 black : 2 brown. This is an example of a

    a. genotypic ratio.
    b. probability equation.
    c. percentage.
    d. phenotypic ratio.

Name _____ Class _____ Date _____

DNA, RNA, AND PROTEIN SYNTHESIS

Section 10-1: Discovery of DNA

Read the passage below, which covers topics from your textbook. Answer the questions that follow.

In the early 1940s, Oswald Avery and his colleagues set out to test whether the transforming agent in Griffith's experiment was protein, RNA, or DNA. The scientists used enzymes to separately destroy each of the three molecules in heat-killed S cells. They used a protease enzyme to destroy protein in heat-killed cells in the first experiment, an enzyme called RNase to destroy RNA in the second experiment, and an enzyme called DNase to destroy DNA in the third experiment. Then they separately mixed the three experimental batches of heat-killed S cells with live R cells and injected mice with the mixtures. The cells missing protein and RNA were able to transform R cells into S cells and kill the mice. However, cells missing DNA did not transform R cells into S cells, and the mice survived.

Read each question and write your answer in the space provided.

SKILL: Recognizing Cause-and-Effect Relationships

In a cause-and-effect relationship, one event, or cause, triggers a second event, or effect, to occur.

1. What enzyme destroys protein?

_____

2. What enzyme destroys DNA?

_____

3. What experimental batch of heat-killed S cells and live R cells resulted in the mice surviving?

_____

Circle the letter of the word or phrase that best completes the statement.

4. In Avery's experiment, R cells were transformed into

    a. protein.   **c.** DNA.

    b. S cells.   **d.** RNA.

CHAPTER 10 ACTIVE READING WORKSHEETS

DNA, RNA, AND PROTEIN SYNTHESIS

Section 10-2: DNA Structure

Read the passage below, which covers topics from your textbook. Answer the questions that follow.

[1] The nucleic acid DNA is an organic compound. [2] DNA is made up of repeating subunits called nucleotides. [3] Each DNA molecule consists of two long chains of nucleotides. [4] A DNA nucleotide has three parts: a sugar molecule called **deoxyribose;** a phosphate group, which consists of a phosphorus, P, atom surrounded by oxygen, O, atoms; and a molecule that is referred to as a **nitrogenous base** because it contains nitrogen, N, atoms. [5] The deoxyribose sugar and the phosphate group are identical in all DNA nucleotides. [6] However, the nitrogenous base may be any one of four different kinds.

[7] The four nitrogenous bases found in DNA nucleotides are adenine, guanine, cytosine, and thymine. [8] It is customary to represent nucleotides by the abbreviations for their nitrogenous bases. [9] A nucleotide containing adenine is represented by *A.* Likewise, C = cytosine, G = guanine, and T = thymine.

Read each question and write your answer in the space provided.

SKILL: Identifying Main Ideas

1. Which sentence notes the main idea of the passage?

   _____

2. What is the main idea of the passage?

   _____

3. What supporting detail does Sentence 3 provide the reader?

   _____

Circle the letter of the word or phrase that best completes the analogy.

4. *G* is to guanine as *C* is to

   a. cell.
   b. nitrogenous base.
   c. adenine.
   d. cytosine.

DNA, RNA, AND PROTEIN SYNTHESIS

Section 10-3: DNA Replication

Read the passage below, which covers topics from your textbook. Answer the questions that follow.

The process of DNA replication occurs in a series of steps. In step 1, enzymes called **helicases** separate the DNA strands. Helicases move along the DNA molecule, breaking hydrogen bonds between the complementary nitrogenous bases. This action allows the two DNA strands of the double helix to separate. The Y-shaped region that results when the two strands separate is called a **replication fork.** During step 2, enzymes called **DNA polymerases** add complementary nucleotides, found floating freely inside the nucleus, to each of the original strands. As the nucleotides on the newly forming strand are added, covalent bonds form between the deoxyribose sugar of one nucleotide and the phosphate group of the next nucleotide on the growing strand. Hydrogen bonds form between the complementary nitrogenous bases on the original and new strands. By step 3, DNA polymerases finish replicating the DNA and fall off. Two new DNA molecules have formed. Each molecule has one original strand and one new strand.

Read each question and write your answer in the space provided.

SKILL: Sequencing Information

1. What happens after a replication fork is formed? _____

_____

_____

2. What event begins the process of DNA replication? _____

_____

_____

Circle the letter of the word or phrase that best completes the statement.

3. Each new DNA molecule has

   a. one new strand and one original strand.   **c.** two original strands.
   b. two new strands.   **d.** None of the above

CHAPTER 10 ACTIVE READING WORKSHEETS

DNA, RNA, AND PROTEIN SYNTHESIS

Section 10-4: Protein Synthesis

Read the passage below, which covers topics from your textbook. Answer the questions that follow.

The genetic information necessary for making proteins is encoded in the sequence of nucleotides in mRNA. A group of three mRNA nucleotides is called a **codon.** Each codon codes for a specific amino acid.

A few codons do not code for amino acids at all. Instead, these codons signal for translation of an mRNA to start or stop. The start codon (AUG) tells a ribosome to start translating an mRNA molecule. Stop codons (UAA, UAG, UGA) cause the ribosome to stop translating an mRNA molecule.

Read each question and write your answer in the space provided.

SKILL: Recognizing Cause-and-Effect Relationships

In a cause-and-effect relationship, one event, or cause, triggers a second event, or effect, to occur.

1. What effect do codons have on protein synthesis?

_____

_____

2. What causes a ribosome to start translating an mRNA molecule?

_____

_____

3. What causes a ribosome to stop translating an mRNA molecule?

_____

Circle the letter of the phrase that best completes the statement.

4. A codon might cause any of the following events to occur EXCEPT

    a. the binding to a molecule with a cell.
    b. the starting of translation.
    c. the coding for an amino acid.
    d. the stopping of translation.

CHAPTER 11 ACTIVE READING WORKSHEETS

GENE EXPRESSION

Section 11-1: Control of Gene Expression

Read the passage below, which covers topics from your textbook. Answer the questions that follow.

Eukaryotic DNA is organized as fibers of chromatin wrapped around small specialized proteins called histones. Prior to mitosis or meiosis, the DNA and histones coil tightly to form chromosomes. After mitosis or meiosis, certain regions of the DNA coils relax, thus making transcription possible. This uncoiled form, known as **euchromatin,** is the site of active transcription of DNA into RNA.

As in prokaryotes, the promoter is the binding site of RNA polymerase. In the eukaryotic gene, there are two kinds of segments beyond the promoter: introns and exons. **Introns** are the sections of a structural gene that are transcribed but not translated. **Exons** are the sections of a structural gene that, when expressed, are transcribed and translated.

Read each question and write your answer in the space provided.

SKILL: Recognizing Similarities and Differences

One reading skill is the ability to recognize similarities and differences between two phrases, ideas, or things. This skill is also known as comparing and contrasting.

1. How does the shape of DNA and histones vary before and after mitosis or meiosis?

_____

2. What is the binding site of RNA polymerase in both prokaryotes and eukaryotes?

_____

Circle the letter of the phrase that best answers the question.

3. What is euchromatin?

    a. a section of a structural gene that codes for amino acids
    b. an uncoiled section of DNA
    c. a unique type of chromosome
    d. a binding site for RNA polymerase

CHAPTER 11 ACTIVE READING WORKSHEETS

GENE EXPRESSION

Section 11-2: Gene Expression in Development and Cell Division

Read the passage below, which covers topics from your textbook. Answer the questions that follow.

A **tumor** is an abnormal proliferation of cells that results from uncontrolled, abnormal cell division. The cells of a *benign tumor* remain within a mass. Examples of benign tumors are the fibroid cysts that occur in a woman's breasts or uterus. Most benign tumors can be removed by surgery.

In a *malignant tumor*, the uncontrolled dividing cells may invade and destroy healthy tissues elsewhere in the body. Malignant tumors are more commonly known as **cancer. Metastasis** is the spread of cancer cells beyond their original site. When metastasis occurs, the cancer cells break away from the malignant tumor and travel to other parts of the body, where they invade healthy tissue and begin forming new tumors. Malignant tumors can be categorized according to the types of tissues they affect. **Carcinomas** grow in the skin and the tissues that line the organs of the body. **Sarcomas** grow in bone and muscle tissue. **Lymphomas** are solid tumors that grow in tissues that form blood cells.

Read each question and write your answer in the space provided.

SKILL: Forming Analogies

In an analogy, one must analyze the relationship between two words and then identify another pair of words that have the same relationship. In the analogy "Glove is to hand as sock is to foot," the relationship is article of clothing to part of the body where worn.

1. Complete the following analogy: "Skin is to carcinoma as bone is to _____."

2. What relationship was used to form the analogy in question 1?

_____

Circle the letter of the word or phrase that best completes the analogy.

3. Sarcomas are to muscle tissue as lymphomas are to

    a. uterus.   **c.** tissues that form blood cells.
    b. lungs.   **d.** Both (a) and (b)

Name _____ Class _____ Date _____

INHERITANCE PATTERNS AND HUMAN GENETICS

Section 12-1: Chromosomes and Inheritance

Read the passage below, which covers topics from your textbook. Answer the questions that follow.

The substitution, addition, or removal of a single nucleotide is a **point mutation,** which is a change that occurs within a single gene or other segment of DNA on a chromosome. In a **substitution,** one nucleotide replaces another. If this substitution occurs in a codon, the amino acid can be changed. In a deletion mutation, one or more nucleotides in a gene are lost. This loss can cause incorrect grouping of the remaining codons, called a **frameshift mutation,** making all amino acids downstream change. This mutation, in turn, can have a disastrous effect on the protein's function. In **insertion mutations,** one or more nucleotides are added to a gene, which can also result in a frameshift mutation.

Write your answers in the spaces provided.

SKILL: Interpreting Graphics

1. Identify the type of mutation illustrated by the figure.

_____

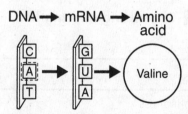

Read the question and write your answer in the space provided.

SKILL: Vocabulary Development

2. The term *mutation* is derived from the Latin word *mutare,* which means "to change." What other terms can be traced to the Latin word *mutare*?

_____

Circle the letter of the phrase that best completes the statement.

3. A point mutation can be caused by
   a. substitution.   **c.** deletion.
   b. addition.   **d.** All of the above

CHAPTER 12 ACTIVE READING WORKSHEETS

INHERITANCE PATTERNS AND HUMAN GENETICS

Section 12-2: Human Genetics

Read the passage below, which covers topics from your textbook. Answer the questions that follow.

One form of colorblindness is a recessive X-linked disorder in which an individual cannot distinguish certain colors. Recall that genes for X-linked traits are found only on the X chromosome. Although many forms of colorblindness exist, the most common is the inability to distinguish red and green. About 8 percent of males are colorblind.

Hemophilia is another recessive X-linked disease that occurs almost exclusively in males. This disorder impairs the ability of blood to clot following a cut, bruise, or other injury. Another recessive X-linked trait in humans is Duchenne muscular dystrophy, a form of muscular dystrophy that weakens and progressively destroys muscle tissue.

Use the passage to complete the exercises below describing X-linked disorders.

SKILL: Organizing Information

Disorder	Symptom
Colorblindness	1.
2.	impaired ability of blood to clot following a cut, bruise, or injury
Duchenne muscular dystrophy	3.

Circle the letter of the phrase that best answers the question.

4. How are all three disorders that are noted in the table alike?

   a. All occur mainly in males.
   b. All are recessive traits.
   c. About 8 percent of the population is affected by these disorders.
   d. All affect muscle tissue.

GENE TECHNOLOGY

Section 13-1: DNA Technology

Read the passage below, which covers topics from your textbook. Answer the questions that follow.

> Restriction enzymes can be used to isolate a specific gene. Once a gene has been isolated, it can be transferred by a vector to an organism. A **vector** is a DNA carrier that is used to clone a gene and can transfer DNA information from one organism to another. Many bacteria contain a cloning vector called a plasmid. A **plasmid** is a ring of DNA found in a bacterium in addition to its main chromosome.
>
> To be used as a cloning vector in recombinant DNA experiments, a plasmid is removed from a bacterium. Using restriction enzymes, the plasmid is then cut and a donor gene—a specific gene isolated from another organism—is spliced into it. Then the plasmid is returned to the bacterium, where it replicates as the bacterium divides and forms an exact copy of the donor gene. The bacteria containing clones of the donor gene can then be used to infect other organisms and transfer the gene to them.

Write your answers in the spaces provided.

SKILL: Sequencing Information

One reading skill is the ability to sequence information, or to logically place items or events in the order in which they occur.

1. Order the statements to show the steps of a recombinant DNA experiment. Write "1" on the line in front of the statement that describes what happens first. Write "2" on the line in front of the statement that describes what happens next, and so on.

_____ **a.** The plasmid is cut with restriction enzymes.

_____ **b.** As the bacterium divides, the donor gene is cloned.

_____ **c.** A donor gene is spliced into the plasmid.

_____ **d.** A plasmid is removed from a bacterium.

_____ **e.** The bacterium transfers the donor gene to other organisms it infects.

_____ **f.** The altered plasmid is returned to the bacterium.

continued on the next page . . .

Write your answers in the spaces provided.

SKILL: Interpreting Graphics

2. The figure below shows the steps of a recombinant DNA experiment. Using information from the passage, write the name of the structure on each lettered line. Use the following labels: "Bacterium," "Donor gene," and "Plasmid." On the numbered lines below the figure, describe what is occurring at each numbered section of the figure.

a._____

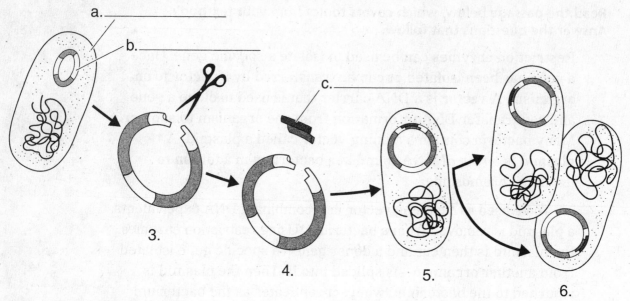

b._____

c._____

3. _____

3. _____

4. _____

5. _____

_____

6. _____

_____

Read the question and write your answer in the space provided.

SKILL: Vocabulary Development

7. What is the meaning of the term *isolate* in the first sentence of the passage?

_____

Circle the letter of the phrase that best completes the statement.

8. A plasmid is a type of

   a. restriction enzyme.
   b. cloning vector.
   c. bacterial main chromosome.
   d. Both (a) and (b)

GENE TECHNOLOGY

Section 13-2: The Human Genome Project

Read the passage below, which covers topics from your textbook. Answer the questions that follow.

As important as genomes are, it is the proteins they encode that actually carry out the work of cells. [1] To understand how genes work, biologists must understand proteins. [2] **Proteomics** is the study of all of an organism's proteins, including their identities, structures, interactions, and abundances. [3] A key tool in proteomics is **two-dimensional gel electrophoresis,** a method that separates the proteins in a sample into individual spots. A researcher can cut out a protein spot from the gel, then use special methods to determine the amino acid sequence in part of the protein. [4] Using a bioinformatic database, he or she can then search the DNA of a sequenced genome and match an individual gene to that unique protein. [5] Proteomics and bioinformatics will allow medical researchers to identify new targets for therapeutic drugs, and develop new markers for diagnosing disease.

Read each question and write your answer in the space provided.

SKILL: Identifying Main Ideas

1. Which sentence identifies the main idea of the passage?

   _____

2. Which sentence identifies future uses of proteomics?

   _____

3. What is the purpose of sentence 2?

   _____

   _____

4. Which sentence implies the use of a computer to obtain results?

   _____

continued on the next page . . .

Read each question and write your answer in the space provided.

SKILL: Vocabulary Development

5. What is the meaning of the term *abundances* in sentence 2?

_____

_____

Circle the letter of the word or phrase that best completes the statement.

6. Two-dimensional gel electrophoresis is a tool that separates

    a. DNA into nucleotides.
    b. proteins into smaller fragments.
    c. amino acids from DNA.
    d. markers in new drugs.

GENE TECHNOLOGY

Section 13-3: Genetic Engineering

Read the passage below, which covers topics from your textbook.
Answer the questions that follow.

Many viral diseases, such as influenza, smallpox, and polio, cannot be treated effectively by existing drugs. Instead, many viral diseases are combated by prevention, using vaccines. A vaccine is a substance that contains a harmless version of a virus or a bacterium. Traditionally, vaccines have been made of disease-causing agents— also called pathogens—that have been treated (chemically or physically) so that they can no longer cause disease. Vaccines can also be produced using active pathogens that carry surface proteins that are the same as or very similar to a more harmful pathogen. When a person contracts the disease or receives a vaccine, his or her body recognizes the pathogen's surface proteins and makes antibodies against the pathogen. In the future, if the same pathogen enters the body, the body is prepared to combat it quickly and to prevent or weaken the pathogen's effects.

On rare occasions a vaccine may cause the disease it is intended to protect people against. Genetic engineering can be used to produce **DNA vaccines,** which may be safer than some traditionally prepared vaccines. The genes for a disease-causing virus's surface proteins can be inserted into a harmless virus. The transplanted genes cause the harmless virus to produce the surface proteins that alert the body to the presence of the disease-causing virus. Genetic engineering can also be used to alter the genome of a pathogen so that it no longer causes a disease. The altered pathogens can then be used as a vaccine against unaltered forms of the pathogen.

Fill in the blank to complete each sentence.

SKILL: Completing Sentences

One reading skill is the ability to complete an incomplete sentence by logically determining what will complete the unfinished thought.

1. Three examples of viral diseases are _____.

continued on the next page . . .

2. Many viral diseases are combated by prevention through _____.

3. A vaccine is a substance that contains a harmless version of a _____.

4. Another name for a disease-causing agent is _____.

5. A pathogen can be chemically or physically treated to eliminate its ability to _____

_____.

6. If a pathogen enters the body of a person who has been vaccinated for that particular virus, the

body will recognize the _____.

7. Sometimes, a vaccine causes the disease _____.

8. One method of producing effective DNA vaccines that are safer than vaccines that are produced

by traditional methods is through_____.

9. Through genetic engineering, genes for a disease-causing virus's surface proteins are inserted

into a _____.

10. Genetic engineering can be used to alter the _____.

11. Pathogens that have been altered so that they no longer cause a disease can be used as a vaccine

against _____.

Read the question and write your answer in the space provided.

SKILL: **Vocabulary Development**

12. What is the meaning of the term *prevention* in the second sentence of the passage?

_____

_____

Circle the letter of the phrase that best completes the statement.

13. A body that recognizes a pathogen's surface proteins has likely

    a. received a vaccination for the disease.
    b. had the disease at an earlier time.
    c. been altered genetically.
    d. Both (a) and (b)

Name _____ Class _____ Date _____

HISTORY OF LIFE

Section 14-1: Biogenesis

The figure below shows the steps in Pasteur's experiment. Study the figure. Then answer the questions that follow.

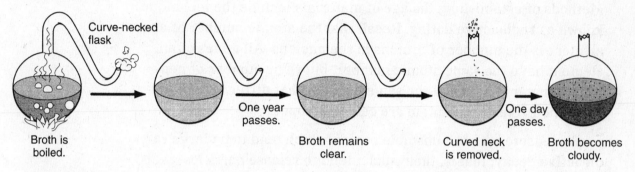

Broth is boiled. One year passes. Broth remains clear. Curved neck is removed. One day passes. Broth becomes cloudy.

Read each question and write your answer in the space provided.

SKILL: Interpreting Graphics

One reading skill is the ability to interpret or understand graphs or tables that may appear in text. The following questions test your ability to interpret information from the figure.

1. What does the first flask contain?

   _____

2. How does the broth change during the experiment?

   _____

   _____

Circle the letter of the phrase that best completes the statement.

3. The experiment illustrated above suggests that

   a. the broth was never properly boiled.
   b. microorganisms in the air contaminated the broth.
   c. the flask must be sealed to prevent contamination.
   d. Both (a) and (b)

Name _____ Class _____ Date _____

HISTORY OF LIFE

Section 14-2: Earth's History

Read the passage below, which covers topics from your textbook. Answer the questions that follow.

Methods of establishing the age of materials include the technique known as **radioactive dating.** Recall that the atomic number of an element is the number of protons in the nucleus. All atoms of an element have the same atomic number, but their number of neutrons can vary. Atoms of the same element that differ in the number of neutrons they contain are called **isotopes.**

Some isotopes have unstable nuclei, which tend to undergo **radioactive decay;** that is, their nuclei tend to release particles, radiant energy, or both. Such isotopes are called **radioactive isotopes.** Rates of decay of radioactive isotopes have been determined for many isotopes. The length of time it takes for one-half of any size sample of an isotope to decay is called its **half-life.**

Read each question and write your answer in the space provided.

SKILL: Identifying Main Ideas

One reading skill is the ability to identify the main idea of a passage. Frequently a main idea is accompanied by supporting information that offers detailed facts about the main idea.

1. What is radioactive dating?

   _____

2. What causes an isotope to undergo radioactive decay?

   _____

3. What does *half-life* refer to?

   _____

Circle the letter of the word or phrase that best completes the sentence.

4. Isotopes undergoing radioactive decay may release
   a. radiant energy.
   b. particles.
   c. carbon.
   d. Both (a) and (b)

CHAPTER 14 ACTIVE READING WORKSHEETS

HISTORY OF LIFE

Section 14-3: The First Life-Forms

Read the passage below, which covers topics from your textbook. Answer the questions that follow.

In the early 1980s, researcher Thomas Cech discovered what he termed a **ribozyme,** an RNA molecule that can act as an enzyme and promote a specific chemical reaction. Hypothetically, a ribozyme could act as an enzyme *and* have the ability to replicate itself.

Recent studies based on Cech's discovery have indicated that life may have started with self-replicating molecules of RNA. RNA molecules would have heredity and would be able to respond to natural selection and thus evolve. Replication—or reproduction of the RNA molecule—might involve competing with other similar RNA molecules for a fixed number of available nucleotides. An RNA molecule that is more successful in getting nucleotides from its environment has an advantage over other RNA molecules. This advantage would then be passed on to the "offspring" of the RNA molecules, the new RNA molecules created by replication.

Read each question and write your answer in the space provided.

SKILL: Recognizing Cause-and-Effect Relationships

1. What might cause a single RNA molecule to respond to natural selection?

   _____

   _____

2. What effect of replication is described in the passage?

   _____

   _____

Circle the letter of the term that best completes the statement.

3. According to researcher Thomas Cech, a ribozyme can
   a. replicate itself.
   b. act as an enzyme.
   c. invade cells.
   d. Both (a) and (b)

Name _____ Class _____ Date _____

THEORY OF EVOLUTION

Section 15-1: History of Evolutionary Thought

Read the passage below, which covers topics from your textbook. Answer the questions that follow.

Darwin used the phrase *descent with modification* to describe the process of evolution. He carefully reviewed the evidence that every species—living or extinct—must have descended by reproduction from preexisting species and that species must be able to change over time. Darwin was not the first person to put forward the idea of descent with modification, but he was the first to argue that *all* species had descended from only one or a few original kinds of life.

Darwin saw the animals of the Galápagos Islands as evidence of descent with modification. For example, the islands are home to 13 similar species of finches. Each of these bird species has a beak that is best adapted for a certain kind of food. But Darwin suspected that all 13 species descended from and diverged from just a few ancestral finches. These ancestors could have flown to the Galápagos Islands from elsewhere sometime after the islands were formed.

Read each question and write your answer in the space provided.

SKILL: Identifying Main Ideas

1. What is descent with modification as used by Darwin?

   _____

   _____

2. What evidence supporting Darwin's descent with modification is contained in the passage?

   _____

   _____

Circle the letter of the phrase that best completes the sentence.

3. According to Darwin's descent with modification, organisms

   a. can exist in only one particular geographic location.

   b. give rise to similar organisms.

   c. do not change over time.

   d. Both (a) and (b)

Name _____ Class _____ Date _____

THEORY OF EVOLUTION

Section 15-2: Evidence of Evolution

Read the passage below, which covers topics from your textbook. Answer the questions that follow.

In 1668, Robert Hooke published his conclusion that fossils are the remains of plants and animals. Hooke was one of the first scientists to study fossils, principally petrified wood, with the aid of a microscope. Hooke thought the detail he saw with the microscope was too fine and precise to have been formed by the rock itself. He hypothesized that living organisms had somehow been turned to rock.

Hooke's view was shared by another scientist of his time, Nicolaus Steno. In 1669, Steno proposed the principle of **superposition,** which states that successive layers of rock or soil were deposited on top of one another by wind or water. The lowest stratum, or layer, in a cross section of Earth is the oldest, while the top stratum is the most recent. Thus, fossils within a single stratum are of the same approximate age. Using Steno's principle, observers could establish the **relative age** of a fossil; that is, they could say that a given fossil was younger or older than another fossil. The fossil's **absolute age** (its age in years) could be estimated from the amount of sediment deposited above the fossil or by using the radiometric dating of a nearby rock layer.

Fill in the blank to complete each sentence.

SKILL: Sentence Completion

One reading skill is the ability to complete an incomplete sentence by logically determining what will complete the unfinished thought.

1. Robert Hooke was one of the first scientists to study fossils through a _____.

2. His observations led Hooke to conclude that fossils are the remains of _____.

3. According to the principle of superposition, fossils in the same stratum are about _____.

Circle the letter of the word or phrase that best completes the statement.

4. The top stratum in a cross section of Earth is the

    a. youngest.   **c.** oldest.

    b. layer most likely to contain fossils.   **d.** Both (a) and (b)

CHAPTER 15 ACTIVE READING WORKSHEETS

THEORY OF EVOLUTION

Section 15-3: Evolution in Action

**Read the passage below, which covers topics from your textbook.
Answer the questions that follow.**

The change of two or more species in close association with each other is called **coevolution.** Predators and their prey sometimes coevolve, parasites and their hosts often coevolve, and plant-eating animals and the plants they feed on also coevolve. One example of coevolution is plants and the animals that pollinate them.

Sometimes, organisms that appear to be very similar, such as a shark and a porpoise, are not closely related at all. This kind of similarity is the result of **convergent evolution.** Convergent evolution occurs when the environment selects similar phenotypes, even though the ancestral types were quite different from each other. Analogous structures, such as similar fins in very different animals, are associated with convergent evolution.

In **divergent evolution,** two or more closely related populations or species become more and more dissimilar. Divergence is nearly always a response to differing environments, and it can ultimately result in new species. Sometimes, the process of divergence can be sped up artificially through **artificial selection.** All domestic dogs are the same species, *Canis familiaris*. Dogs have been bred by humans for certain phenotypic characteristics, resulting in different breeds with different traits.

Refer to the passage to complete the graphic organizer below.

SKILL: Organizing Information

Patterns of Evolution		
Evolution	**Pattern definition**	**Example**
1.	3.	parasites and their hosts
Convergent evolution	4.	5.
2.	two or more related species or populations become more and more dissimilar, often due to differing habitats	6.

continued on the next page . . .

Circle the letter of the word or phrase that best completes the sentence.

7. Artificial selection can sometimes speed up the process of
   a. convergent evolution.
   b. coevolution.
   c. divergent evolution.
   d. Both (a) and (b)

Modern Biology Active Reading Worksheets   Section 15-3

Name _____ Class _____ Date _____

POPULATION GENETICS AND SPECIATION

Section 16-1: Genetic Equilibrium

The figure below shows how phenotype can change from generation to generation of four o'clock flowers. Homozygous *RR* flowers are red. Homozygous *rr* flowers are white. Heterozygous *Rr* flowers are pink rather than red. Use the figure to answer the questions that follow.

FIRST GENERATION

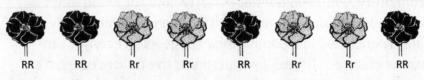

RR   RR   Rr   Rr   RR   Rr   Rr   RR

SECOND GENERATION

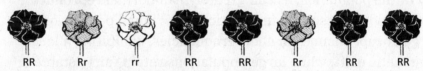

RR   Rr   rr   RR   RR   Rr   RR   RR

Read each question and write your answer in the space provided.

SKILL: Recognizing Similarities and Differences

1. A **phenotype frequency** is equal to the number of individuals with a particular phenotype divided by the total number of individuals in the population. Compare the phenotype frequency of the first and second generations.

   _____

   _____

2. **Allele frequency** is determined by dividing the number of a certain allele by the total number of alleles of all types in the population. Compare the allele frequency of the first and second generations.

   _____

Circle the letter that best completes the sentence.

3. The phenotype of a pink four o'clock flower is
   a. *RR.*
   b. *Rr.*
   c. *rr.*
   d. Either (a) or (b)

CHAPTER 16 ACTIVE READING WORKSHEETS

POPULATION GENETICS
AND SPECIATION

Section 16-2: Disruption of Genetic Equilibrium

Read the passage below, which covers topics from your textbook. Answer the questions that follow.

[1] The third requirement of genetic equilibrium is the presence of a large population. [2] The Hardy-Weinberg principle is based on the laws of probability, which do not necessarily hold for small and medium-sized populations. [3] **Genetic drift** is the phenomenon by which allele frequencies in a population change as a result of random events, or chance. [4] In small populations, the failure of even a single organism to reproduce can significantly disrupt the allele frequency of the population, as can greater-than-normal reproduction by an individual, resulting in genetic drift. [5] Small populations can undergo abrupt changes in allele frequencies, exhibiting a large degree of genetic drift, while large populations retain fairly stable allele frequencies, maintaining a small degree of genetic drift.

Read each question and write your answer in the space provided.

SKILL: Identifying Main Ideas

1. Which sentence identifies the main idea of this passage?

_____

2. What is this main idea?

_____

_____

Circle the letter of the phrase that best completes the statement.

3. A correlation exists between the size of a population and

   a. its degree of genetic drift.
   b. the likelihood of greater-than-normal reproduction by its members.
   c. the probability that a member will fail to reproduce.
   d. Both (a) and (b)

POPULATION GENETICS AND SPECIATION

Section 16-3: Formation of Species

Read the passage below, which covers topics from your textbook. Answer the questions that follow.

Sometimes groups of organisms within a population become genetically isolated without being geographically isolated. **Reproductive isolation** results from barriers to successful breeding between population groups in the same area. In disruptive selection, the two extremes of a trait in a given population are selected for and the organisms begin to diverge. Once successful mating is prevented between members of two subpopulations, the effect is the same as what would have occurred if the two subpopulations had been geographically isolated. There are two broad types of reproductive isolation: **prezygotic isolation,** which occurs *before* fertilization, and **postzygotic isolation,** which occurs *after* fertilization.

Read each question and write your answer in the space provided.

SKILL: Forming Analogies

In the analogy "Glove is to hand as sock is to foot," the relationship is article of clothing to part of the body on which it is worn.

1. What relationship was used to form the analogy "Geographic isolation is to physical separation as reproductive isolation is to breeding barriers"?

   _____

2. Complete the following analogy: "Before is to prezygotic isolation as after is to

   _____."

Circle the letter of the phrase that best completes the statement.

3. Prevention of successful mating between members of two subpopulations may result in

   a. geographic isolation.   **c.** reproductive isolation.
   b. disruptive selection.   **d.** Both (a) and (b)

Name _____ Class _____ Date _____

CLASSIFICATION OF ORGANISMS

Section 17-1: Biodiversity

**Read the passage below, which covers topics from your textbook.
Answer the questions that follow.**

Linnaeus divised a nested hierarchy of seven different levels of organization. Linnaeus's largest category is called a **kingdom.** There are two kingdoms, plant and animal, which are the same as Aristotle's main categories. Each subset within a kingdom is known as a **phylum,** in the animal kingdom, or a **division,** in the plant kingdom. Within a phylum or division, each subset is called a **class,** and each subset within a class is called an **order.** Still smaller groupings are the **family** and the **genus.** The smallest grouping of all, which contains only a single organism type, is known as the **species.**

In Linnaeus's system, the species name (also called the scientific name) of an organism has two parts. The first part of the name is the genus, and the second part is the *species identifier*, usually a descriptive word. Thus, we humans are known by our genus, *Homo*, and by our species identifier, *sapiens*. This system of two-part names is known as **binomial nomenclature.**

Read each question and write your answer in the space provided.

SKILL: Forming Analogies

An analogy identifies a similar relationship between different pairs of items.

1. Complete the following analogy: "Plant is to division as animal is to _____."

2. Complete the following analogy: "*Homo* is to genus as *sapiens* is to _____."

Circle the letter of the word that best completes the analogy.

3. Class is to order as order is to

   a. division.
   b. family.
   c. kingdom.
   d. phylum.

CLASSIFICATION OF ORGANISMS

Section 17-2: Systematics

Read the passage below, which covers topics from your textbook. Answer the questions that follow.

One relatively new system of phylogenetic classification is called **cladistics.** Cladistics uses certain features of organisms, called shared derived characters, to establish evolutionary relationships. A **derived character** is a feature that apparently evolved only within the group under consideration. For example, if the group being considered is birds, one example of a derived characteristic is feathers. Most animals do not have feathers; birds are the only animals that do. Therefore, it is safe to assume that feathers evolved within the bird group and were not inherited from some distant ancestor of the birds.

Cladistic taxonomists agree that organisms that share a derived character—like feathers—probably share it because they inherited it from a common ancestor. So shared derived characters, particularly a *group* of several shared derived characters, are strong evidence of common ancestry between organisms that share them. Ancestry diagrams made by means of cladistic analysis are called **cladograms.**

Read each question and write your answer in the space provided.

SKILL: Identifying Main Ideas

1. What is the main idea of the passage?

   _____

2. What derived character is identified in the passage?

   _____

Circle the letter of the phrase that best completes the statement.

3. As the number of shared derived characters increases among organisms, the likelihood that the organisms

   a. lack a common ancestry increases.   **c.** share a common ancestry increases.

   b. belong to the same species increases.   **d.** Both (b) and (c)

CLASSIFICATION OF ORGANISMS

Section 17-3: Modern Classification

Observe the figure below, which covers topics from your textbook.
Answer the questions that follow.

Six Kingdoms of Life			
Kingdom	**Cell type**	**Number of cells**	**Nutrition**
Archaea	prokaryotic	unicellular	autotrophy and heterotrophy
Bacteria	prokaryotic	unicellular	autotrophy and heterotrophy
Protista	eukaryotic	unicellular and multicellular	autotrophy and heterotrophy
Fungi	eukaryotic	unicellular and multicellular	heterotrophy
Plantae	eukaryotic	multicellular	autotrophy and (rarely) heterotrophy
Animalia	eukaryotic	multicellular	heterotrophy

Read each question and write your answer in the space provided.

SKILL: Organizing Information

One reading skill is the ability to organize and interpret information, which means the ability to use or interpret tables and graphic organizers.

1. For which two kingdoms are all column entries exactly the same?

   _____

2. What is the only difference in the column entries for kingdoms Fungi and Animalia?

   _____

   _____

Circle the letter of the word that best completes the analogy.

3. Unicellular is to Archaea as multicellular is to

   a. Protista.
   b. Fungi.
   c. Bacteria.
   d. Plantae.

INTRODUCTION TO ECOLOGY

Section 18-1: Introduction to Ecology

Read the passage below, which covers topics from your textbook. Answer the questions that follow.

All organisms interact with other organisms in their surroundings and with the nonliving portion of their environment. Their survival depends on these interactions. Ecologists refer to this quality as *interconnectedness* or **interdependence.**

Interdependence is a key theme found throughout ecology. For example, you could not survive without the plants and other photosynthetic organisms that produce oxygen. Your cells need oxygen to release the energy in food, and cells will die if deprived of oxygen for even a few minutes. Conversely, photosynthetic organisms depend on the release of carbon dioxide by the cellular respiration of other organisms, such as humans, and geochemical processes, such as volcanic eruptions. Carbon dioxide gas is an essential raw material for making carbohydrates by photosynthesizers.

Read each question and write your answer in the space provided.

SKILL: Identifying Main Ideas

1. For what function do photosynthetic organisms use carbon dioxide?

   _____

2. What main topic in ecology does the passage discuss?

   _____

   _____

Circle the letter of the phrase that best completes the statement.

3. Photosynthetic organisms depend on carbon dioxide produced by
   a. photosynthesis.
   b. volcanic eruptions.
   c. cellular respiration.
   d. both b and c.

Name _____ Class _____ Date _____

INTRODUCTION TO ECOLOGY

Section 18-2: Ecology of Organisms

Read the passage below, which covers topics from your textbook. Answer the questions that follow.

Ecologists separate the environmental factors that influence an organism into two classes. The living components of the environment are called **biotic factors.** Biotic factors include all of the living things that affect the organism. The nonliving factors, called **abiotic factors,** are the physical and chemical characteristics of the environment. Important abiotic factors include temperature, humidity, pH, salinity, oxygen concentration, amount of sunlight, availability of nitrogen, and precipitation. The importance of each factor varies from environment to environment.

Read each question and write your answer in the space provided.

SKILL: Recognizing Similarities and Differences

1. What are the similarities and differences between biotic factors and abiotic factors?

_____

_____

Read each question and write your answer in the space provided.

SKILL: Vocabulary Development

2. How does the meaning of the word *factors* in the passage differ from its meaning in a mathematics class?

_____

_____

Circle the letter of the word or phrase that best completes the sentence.

3. All of the following are classified as abiotic factors EXCEPT

    a. pH.
    b. bacteria.
    c. salinity.
    d. oxygen concentration.

CHAPTER 18 ACTIVE READING WORKSHEETS

INTRODUCTION TO ECOLOGY

Section 18-3: Energy Transfer

Read the passage below, which covers topics from your textbook. Answer the questions that follow.

Autotrophs, which include plants and some kinds of protists and bacteria, manufacture their own food. Because autotrophs capture energy and use it to make organic molecules, they are called **producers.** Most producers are photosynthetic, so they use solar energy to power the production of food. However, some autotrophic bacteria do not use sunlight as an energy source. These bacteria carry out **chemosynthesis,** which means they produce carbohydrates by using energy from inorganic molecules.

All animals, most protists, all fungi, and many bacteria are heterotrophs. Unlike autotrophs, heterotrophs cannot manufacture their own food. Instead they get energy by eating other organisms or organic wastes. Ecologically speaking, heterotrophs are **consumers.** They obtain energy by consuming organic molecules made by other organisms.

Read each question and write your answer in the space provided.

SKILL: Recognizing Similarities and Differences

1. By what two different means do autotrophs produce their food sources?

   _____

   _____

2. What is the difference between consumers and producers?

   _____

   _____

   _____

Circle the letter of the phrase that best completes the sentence.

3. All of the following are classified as consumers EXCEPT

   a. most protists.
   b. all fungi.
   c. all animals.
   d. all plants.

Name _____ Class _____ Date _____

INTRODUCTION TO ECOLOGY

Section 18-4: Ecosystem Recycling

Read the passage below, which covers topics from your textbook. Answer the questions that follow.

All organisms need nitrogen to make proteins and nucleic acids. The complex pathway that nitrogen follows within an ecosystem is called the **nitrogen cycle.** However, most plant can use nitrogen only in the form of nitrate. The process of converting nitrogen gas to nitrate is called **nitrogen fixation.** Organisms rely on the actions of **nitrogen-fixing bacteria** that are able to transform nitrogen gas into a usable form. Nitrogen-fixing bacteria live in the soil and in the roots of some kinds of plants, such as beans, peas, clover, and alfalfa.

Decomposers break down the corpses and wastes of organisms and release the nitrogen they contain as ammonia, NH_3, which in soil becomes ammonium, NH_4^+. This process is known as **ammonification.** Through ammonification, nitrogen that would otherwise be lost is reintroduced into the ecosystem. Bacteria in the soil take up the ammonium and oxidize it into nitrites, NO_2^-, and nitrates, NO_3^-. This process is called **nitrification.** The erosion of nitrate-rich rocks also releases nitrates into an ecosystem. Plants use nitrates to form amino acids. Nitrogen is returned to the atmosphere through **denitrification.** Denitrification occurs when anaerobic bacteria break down nitrates and release nitrogen gas back into the atmosphere.

Write your answers in the spaces provided.

SKILL: Sequencing Information

1. Order the statements to show the steps by which nitrogen is recycled within an ecosystem. Write "1" on the line in front of the statement that describes what happens first. Write "2" on the line in front of the statement that describes what happens next, and so on.

_____ **a.** Bacteria in the soil oxidize the ammonia into nitrites and nitrates.

_____ **b.** Plants use nitrates to form amino acids.

_____ **c.** Decomposers break down corpses and wastes of organisms.

_____ **d.** Nitrogen is released into the ecosystem as ammonia.

Complete the sentence by logically finishing the thought.

SKILL: Completing Sentences

2. The process by which bacteria in soil oxidize ammonium to form nitrates and nitrites is known as

_____.

3. Denitrification occurs when _____ break down nitrates and release nitrogen gas back into the atmosphere.

4. Nitrogen fixation is the process of converting _____ to nitrate.

5. The organisms that convert nitrogen gas to nitrate are known as _____

_____.

6. The nitrogen cycle is the pathway through which nitrogen flows within a(n) _____.

Read the question and write your answer in the space provided.

SKILL: Vocabulary Development

7. The suffix -*tion* means "the act or state of." How does knowledge of this word part aid in decoding the word *ammonification*?

_____

Circle the letter of the phrase that best completes the statement.

8. All organisms need nitrogen to
   a. make proteins.
   b. make nucleic acids.
   c. produce ammonia.
   d. Both (a) and (b)

POPULATIONS

Section 19-1: Understanding Populations

Read the passage below, which covers topics from your textbook. Answer the questions that follow.

Dispersion is the spatial distribution of individuals within a population. In a clumped distribution, individuals are clustered together. In an even distribution, individuals are separated by a fairly consistent distance. In a random distribution, each individual's location is independent of the locations of the other individuals in the population. Clumped distributions often occur when resources such as food or living space are clumped. Clumped distributions may also occur because of a species' social behavior, such as when zebras gather into herds or birds form flocks. Even distributions usually result from social interactions, but the interactions result in individuals getting as far away from each other as possible.

Write your answers in the spaces provided.

SKILL: Interpreting Graphics

1. On the lines beneath each of the three figures, indicate whether each part of the figure represents a clumped distribution, an even distribution, or a random distribution.

 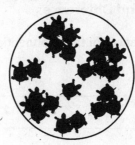 

a. _____ b. _____ c. _____

Read the question and write your answer in the space provided.

SKILL: Vocabulary Development

2. What is the meaning of *consistent* in the passage? _____

Circle the letter of the phrase that best completes the statement.

3. A flock of migrating birds demonstrates

    a. clumped distribution.   **c.** even distribution.

    b. random distribution.   **d.** Both (a) and (b)

Name _____ Class _____ Date _____

POPULATIONS

Section 19-2: Measuring Populations

Read the passage below, which covers topics from your textbook. Answer the questions that follow.

The **exponential model** of population growth describes a population that increases rapidly after only a few generations; the larger the population gets, the faster it grows. This is called **exponential growth.** In the construction of an exponential model of population growth, it is assumed that birth rates and death rates remain constant, however large the population becomes.

The **logistic model** of population growth builds on the exponential model but accounts for the influence of limiting factors which restrain growth. Birthrates and death rates are not constant, but vary with population size; birthrates decline and death rates rise as the population grows. The logistic model includes a new term, **carrying capacity** (symbolized by K), the number of individuals the environment can support over time.

Read the question and write your answer in the space provided.

SKILL: Recognizing Similarities and Differences

1. What are the similarities and differences of the exponential model and logistic model of population growth?

   _____

   _____

   _____

Read the question and write your answer in the space provided.

SKILL: Vocabulary Development

2. What is the meaning of *restrain* in the passage? _____

Circle the letter of the phrase that best completes the statement.

3. Carrying capacity refers to the number of

   a. females in a population.
   b. abiotic factors in an environment.
   c. individuals an environment can support over time.
   d. populations present in a particular environment.

CHAPTER 19 ACTIVE READING WORKSHEETS

POPULATIONS

Section 19-3: Human Population Growth

Read the passage below, which covers topics from your textbook.
Answer the questions that follow.

Today about 20 percent of the world's population live in **developed countries.** This category includes all of the world's modern, industrialized countries, such as the United States, Japan, Germany, France, the United Kingdom, Australia, Canada, and Russia. On average, people in developed countries are better educated, healthier, and live longer than the rest of the world's population. Population growth rates in developed countries are very low—about 0.003 per capita. The populations of some of these countries, such as Russia, Germany, and Italy, are shrinking because death rates exceed birthrates.

Most people (about 80 percent of the world's population) live in **developing countries,** a category that includes most countries in Asia, Central America, South America, and Africa. In general, these countries are poorer than the more-developed countries, and their populations are growing much faster—at a growth rate of about 0.015 per capita.

Fill in the blank to complete each sentence.

SKILL: Completing Sentences

1. Today, about 80 percent of the world's population live in _____.

2. Because it is an industrialized country, the United States is classified as a _____.

3. Population growth rates in developed countries are about _____.

4. The population of Germany is shrinking because death rates _____.

5. Population growth rates in developing countries are about _____.

Circle the letter of the word that best completes the analogy.

6. In terms of population growth, North America is to South America as Japan is to

   a. Africa.
   b. Italy.
   c. Australia.
   d. Both (a) and (b)

Name _____ Class _____ Date _____

COMMUNITY ECOLOGY

Section 20-1: Species Interactions

**Read the passage below, which covers topics from your textbook.
Answer the questions that follow.**

Mutualism is a cooperative relationship in which both species derive some benefit. Some mutualistic relationships are so close that neither species can survive without the other.

Commensalism is an interaction in which one species benefits and the other is not affected. Some cases of commensalism may be mutualisms in which the benefit to the second organism hasn't yet been identified.

Read each question and write your answer in the space provided.

SKILL: Recognizing Text Structure

Some of the patterns of text structure you may have seen in earlier sections are similarities and differences, cause and effect, and sequencing information.

1. Which pattern of text structure did the writer use in the above passage?

_____

_____

Read the question and write your answer in the space provided.

SKILL: Vocabulary Development

2. What is the meaning of the term *derive* in the passage?

_____

_____

Circle the letter of the phrase that best completes the statement.

3. Some cases of commensalism may

   a. benefit both organisms.
   b. lack an observable benefit for either organism.
   c. harm both organisms.
   d. Both (a) and (b)

CHAPTER 20 ACTIVE READING WORKSHEETS

COMMUNITY ECOLOGY

Section 20-2: Patterns in Communities

Read the passage below, which covers topics from your textbook. Answer the questions that follow.

Another pattern of species richness is that larger areas usually contain more species than smaller areas do. This relationship is called the **species-area effect.** The species-area effect is most often applied to islands, where area is clearly limited by geography. In the Caribbean, for example, more species of reptiles and amphibians live on large islands, such as Cuba, than on small islands, such as Redonda. Larger areas usually contain a greater diversity of habitats and thus can support more species.

The species-area effect has one very important practical consequence—reducing the size of a habitat reduces the number of species it can support. Today, natural habitats are shrinking rapidly due to the ever-growing human population. The inevitable result of the destruction of habitats is the extinction of species.

Read each question and write your answer in the space provided.

SKILL: Recognizing Text Structure

Some of the patterns of text structure you may have seen in earlier sections are similarities and differences, cause and effect, and sequencing information.

1. Which pattern of text structure did the writer use in the above passage?

   _____

2. What effect of habitat destruction is identified in the passage?

   _____

Circle the letter of the phrase that best completes the statement.

3. The island of Hispaniola is about 1,000 times larger than the island of Saba. According to the passage, one would likely find

   a. a greater degree of species richness on Saba.
   b. equal numbers of species on Saba and Hispaniola.
   c. a greater degree of species richness on Hispaniola.
   d. a greater variation in habitat on Saba.

Read the passage below, which covers topics from your textbook.
Answer the questions that follow.

Ecologists recognize two types of succession. **Primary succession** is the development of a community in an area that has not supported life previously, such as bare rock, a sand dune, or an island formed by a volcanic eruption. **Secondary succession** is the sequential replacement of a species that follows disruption of an existing community. The disruption may stem from a natural disaster, such as a forest fire or a strong storm, or from human activities, such as farming, logging, or mining.

Any new habitat is an invitation to many species that are adapted to be good pioneers. The species that predominate early in succession—called the **pioneer species**—tend to be small, fast-growing, and fast-reproducing. Pioneer species are well suited for invading and occupying a disturbed habitat. They are often very good at dispersing their seeds, which enables them to quickly reach disrupted areas.

Fill in the blank to complete each sentence.

SKILL: Sentence Completion

Complete the sentence by logically finishing the thought.

4. The development of a community in an area that has not supported life previously is classified as

_____ .

5. Human activities that might cause secondary succession include mining, logging, and _____ .

6. Pioneer species are often very good at dispersing _____ .

Circle the letter of the phrase that best completes the analogy.

7. Secondary succession is to a forest that has been destroyed by fire as primary succession is to a

   a. sand dune.
   b. bare rock.
   c. violent storm.
   d. Both (a) and (b)

CHAPTER 21 ACTIVE READING WORKSHEETS

ECOSYSTEMS

Section 21-1: Terrestrial Biomes

Observe the table below, which covers topics from your textbook.
Answer the questions that follow.

Biome	Average yearly temperature range	Average yearly precipitation	Soil	Vegetation
Tundra	−26°C to 12°C	<25 cm	moist, thin topsoil over permafrost; nutrient-poor; slightly acidic	mosses, lichens, grasses, and dwarf woody plants
Taiga	−10°C to 14°C	35–75 cm	low in nutrients; highly acidic	coniferous evergreen trees
Temperate forest	6°C to 28°C	75–125 cm	moist; moderate nutrient levels	broad-leaved trees and shrubs
Temperate grassland	0°C to 25°C	25–75 cm	deep layer of topsoil; very rich in nutrients	dense, tall grasses in moist areas; short clumped grasses in drier areas
Desert	7°C to 38°C	<25 cm	dry, often sandy; nutrient-poor	succulent plants and scattered grasses
Savanna	16°C to 34°C	75–150 cm	dry, thin topsoil; porous; low in nutrients	tall grasses, scattered trees
Tropical forest	20°C to 34°C	200–400 cm	moist, thin topsoil; low in nutrients	broad-leaved evergreen trees and shrubs

Characteristics of Some Major Biomes

Fill in the blank to complete each sentence.

SKILL: Completing Sentences

1. The biomes that receive less than 25 cm of rain per year are _____ .

2. The biome where the soil is porous is the _____ .

Circle the letter of the word or phrase that best completes the analogy.

3. Tall grasses are to savanna as mosses are to

   a. taiga.
   b. temperate forest.
   c. tundra.
   d. tropical forest.

Name _____ Class _____ Date _____

ECOSYSTEMS

Section 21-2: Aquatic Ecosystems

Read the passage below, which covers topics from your textbook. Answer the questions that follow.

The ocean covers about 70 percent of Earth's surface and has an average depth of 3.7 km (2.3 mi). The deepest parts of the ocean are about 11 km (6.8 mi) deep. The water contains about 3 percent salt, mostly sodium chloride, a factor that profoundly affects the biology of the organisms that live there. Another important variable affecting marine organisms is the availability of light. Because water absorbs light, sunlight penetrates only the upper few hundred meters of the ocean. The **photic zone** is the part of the ocean that receives sunlight. The rest of the ocean falls in the **aphotic zone**, the cold and dark depths where sunlight cannot penetrate. Photosynthesis cannot occur in the aphotic zone because of the lack of sunlight.

Ecologists recognize three zones extending out from land. Along ocean shores, the tides produce a rhythmic rise and fall of the water level in an area called the **intertidal zone.** Farther out is the **neritic zone,** which extends over the continental shelf. The water in the neritic zone is relatively shallow (no more than a few hundred feet deep). Beyond the continental shelf is the **oceanic zone,** which is the deep water of the open sea. The neritic and oceanic zones are further divided. The open ocean is known as the **pelagic zone,** while the ocean bottom is known as the **benthic zone.**

Read each question and write your answer in the space provided.

SKILL: Identifying Main Ideas

1. About what percentage of Earth's surface is covered by oceans?

_____

2. What are the three ocean zones that extend out from land?

_____

3. How does the oceanic zone differ from the other two ocean zones?

_____

4. What are the similarities and differences between the pelagic zone and the benthic zone?

_____

_____

_____

_____

5. The figure below shows the various zones of the ocean. On the lettered lines below the figure, write the label that describes what is indicated by the corresponding letter on the figure. You will use the labels: "Aphotic zone," "Benthic zone," "Intertidal zone," "Neritic zone," "Oceanic zone," and "Pelagic zone."

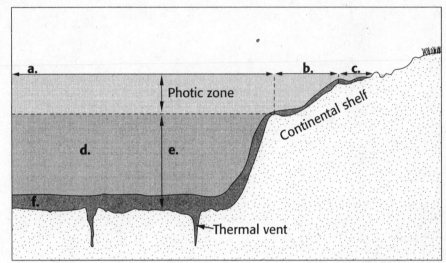

a. _____ d. _____

b. _____ e. _____

c. _____ f. _____

Read the question and write your answer in the space provided.

SKILL: Vocabulary Development

6. What is the meaning of the term *variable* in this passage?

_____

Circle the letter of the phrase that best completes the sentence.

7. The deepest parts of Earth's oceans are about

    a. 6.8 km deep.

    b. 3.7 km deep.

    c. 11 km deep.

    d. 23 km deep.

HUMANS AND THE ENVIRONMENT

Section 22-1: An Interconnected Planet

Read the passage below, which covers topics from your textbook. Answer the questions that follow.

Biodiversity refers to the variety of forms of life in an area. Biodiversity provides important benefits to people. For example, thousands of plant and animal species can serve as food. Trees provide food for homes and fuel. Many species are sources of medicines and useful chemicals. Undiscovered species may someday supply other benefits. And ecosystems recycle human wastes, including CO_2. Writing about such benefits, biologist E. O. Wilson stated, "Biological diversity is the key to the maintenance of the world as we know it."

Some people think that organisms and ecosystems are important for reasons other than their use to humans. These opinions may be based on moral, aesthetic, or religious beliefs that are beyond the scope of biology. People may value biodiversity for multiple reasons.

Read each question and write your answer in the space provided.

SKILL: Identifying Main Ideas

1. What benefits to people are provided by plant species?

   _____

   _____

2. Who said, "Biological diversity is the key to the maintenance of the world as we know it"?

   _____

   _____

Circle the letter of the phrase that best completes the statement.

3. The variety of life forms in an area is known as

   a. the ecosystem diversity.
   b. genetic diversity.
   c. the beneficial species.
   d. biodiversity.

CHAPTER 22 ACTIVE READING WORKSHEETS

HUMANS AND THE ENVIRONMENT

Section 22-2: Environmental Issues

Read the passage below, which covers topics from your textbook. Answer the questions that follow.

Beginning in the 1980s, scientists discovered thinning areas in the ozone layer over Earth's polar regions and declining ozone levels elsewhere in the layer. An international study estimated that a 10 percent drop in ozone levels would cause 300,000 new cases of human skin cancer worldwide. UV light also harms plants and photosynthetic algae, so ozone depletion could modify entire ecosystems over time.

Damage to the ozone layer led most countries to stop producing CFCs by 1995. Environmental scientists estimate that it will take the ozone layer 50 to 100 years to recover completely. The effort to protect the ozone layer shows that scientists, the public, and policy makers can work together to solve environmental problems.

Read each question and write your answer in the space provided.

SKILL: Identifying Main Ideas

1. What effects may result from thinning areas in the ozone layer?

_____

_____

SKILL: Vocabulary Development

2. What is the meaning of the term *depletion* in the passage?

_____

Circle the letter of the phrase that best completes the statement.

3. Chlorofluorocarbons were banned by most countries in

   a. the 1980s.   **c.** the 1990s.
   b. 2000.   **d.** the 1970s.

CHAPTER 22 ACTIVE READING WORKSHEETS

HUMANS AND THE ENVIRONMENT

Section 22-3: Environmental Solutions

Read the passage below, which covers topics from your textbook. Answer the questions that follow.

In the United States during the last 200 years, over 99 percent of native prairies have been replaced with farmland or urban development, and most of the old-growth forests have been cut. Loss of so much of these vegetation types has meant losses of biodiversity.

A discipline, called **conservation biology,** seeks to identify, protect, and manage natural areas. In areas where human influence is greater—such as agricultural areas, former strip mines, and drained wetlands—biologists may have to reverse major changes and replace missing ecosystem components. For example, returning a strip-mined area to a grassland may involve recontouring the land surface, reintroducing bacteria to the soil, planting grass and shrub seedlings, and even using periodic controlled fires to manage the growth of vegetation. Dealing with a more extreme case like this is called **restoration biology.**

Read each question and write your answer in the space provided.

SKILL: Identifying Main Ideas

1. What effect of human population growth is identified in the first paragraph?

_____

SKILL: Vocabulary Development

2. What is the meaning of the term *discipline* in this passage?

_____

Circle the letter of the phrase that best answers the question.

3. Which of the following describes a likely task of a restoration biologist?

    a. raising funds needed to create a national park
    b. returning missing ecosystem components to a drained wetland
    c. educating citizens about the need to protect a local habitat
    d. both (a) and (b)

BACTERIA

Section 23-1: Prokaryotes

Read the passage below, which covers topics from your textbook. Answer the questions that follow.

Scientists treat archaea as a separate domain because these organisms are so different from bacteria. **Methanogens,** a broad phylogenetic group of archaea, are named for their unique method of harvesting energy by converting H_2 and CO_2 into methane gas. Because oxygen is a poison to them, methanogens can live only in anaerobic conditions, such as the bottom of a swamp and in sewage, where they are the source of marsh gas. They can also be found thriving in the intestinal tracts of humans and other animals, such as cows.

Halophiles, which are salt-loving archaea, live in environments with very high salt concentrations, such as the Great Salt Lake and the Dead Sea. High salt concentrations would kill most bacteria, but this high concentration is beneficial to the growth of halophiles.

Thermoacidophiles, a third group of archaea, live in extremely acidic environments that have high temperatures, such as hot springs. Some thermoacidophiles thrive at temperatures up to 110°C (230°F) and at a pH of less than 2. Thermoacidophiles also live near volcanic vents on land or near hydrothermal vents, cracks in the ocean floor that leak scalding acidic water.

Read each question and write your answer in the space provided.

SKILL: Forming Analogies

1. Complete the following analogy: "High salt concentrations are to halophiles as high temperature and acid conditions are to _____."

Circle the letter of the word or phrase that best completes the analogy.

2. Thermoacidophiles are to hot springs as methanogens are to

   a. volcanic vents.   **c.** swamps.
   b. salt water.   **d.** water bodies.

Name _____ Class _____ Date _____

BACTERIA

Section 23-2: Biology of Prokaryotes

Look at the table below, which covers topics from your textbook.
Answer the questions that follow.

Structural Characteristics of a Bacterial Cell	
Structure	**Function**
Cell wall	protects the cell and gives it shape
Outer membrane	protects the cell against some antibiotics (only present in Gram-negative cells)
Cell membrane	regulates movement of materials into and out of the cell; contains enzymes important to cellular respiration
Cytoplasm	contains DNA, ribosomes, and organic compounds required to carry out life processes
Chromosome	carries genetic information inherited from past generations
Plasmid	contains some genes obtained through genetic recombination
Capsule and slime layer	protect the cell and assist in attaching the cell to other surfaces
Endospore	protects the cell against harsh environmental conditions, such as heat and drought
Pilus	assists the cell in attaching to other surfaces, which is important for genetic recombination
Flagellum	moves the cell

Read each question and write your answer in the space provided.

SKILL: Forming Analogies

1. Complete the following analogy: "Enzymes are to cell membrane as DNA is to _____

   _____."

2. Complete the following analogy: "Antibiotics are to outer membrane as heat is to _____

   _____."

Circle the letter of the phrase that best completes the statement.

3. Structures of a bacterial cell that assist in attaching the cell to other surfaces are the

   a. cell wall, plasmid, and capsule.
   b. cytoplasm, outer membrane, and pilus.
   c. chromosome, flagellum, and capsule.
   d. pilus, capsule, and slime layer.

CHAPTER 23 ACTIVE READING WORKSHEETS

BACTERIA

Section 23-3: Bacteria and Humans

**Read the passage below, which covers topics from your textbook.
Answer the questions that follow.**

The scientific study of disease is called **pathology.** Bacteria that cause disease are called pathogens. Some bacteria cause disease by producing poisons called toxins. **Exotoxins** are toxins that are made of protein. Exotoxins are produced by Gram-positive bacteria and are secreted into the surrounding environment. For example, tetanus is a disease caused by an exotoxin.

Endotoxins, toxins made of lipids and carbohydrates, are associated with the outer membrane of Gram-negative bacteria, such as *E. coli.* While exotoxins are steadily released by living Gram-positive bacteria, endotoxins are not released by Gram-negative bacteria until the bacteria die. Once released, endotoxins cause fever, body aches, and weakness, and they damage the vessels of the circulatory system.

Read each question and write your answer in the space provided.

SKILL: Identifying Main Ideas

1. What is the main idea of this passage?

   _____

Read the question and write your answer in the space provided.

SKILL: Vocabulary Development

2. The term *pathogen* comes from the Greek word *pathos,* which means "suffering." How is the term *pathogen* related to its word of origin?

   _____

   _____

Circle the letter of the word or phrase that best completes the sentence.

3. An example of a disease caused by Gram-positive bacteria is

   a. tetanus.   **c.** cancer.
   b. *E. coli.*   **d.** Both (a) and (b)

CHAPTER 24 ACTIVE READING WORKSHEETS

VIRUSES

Section 24-1: Viral Structure and Replication

Read the passage below, which covers topics from your textbook. Answer the questions that follow.

Bacteriophages are composed of a hexagonal head that contains DNA. Beneath the head is a contractile tail that includes a collar and a sheath. The contractile tail helps inject the nucleic acid into the host cell. The tail rests on a base plate from which tail fibers emerge. These fibers assist the virus in attaching to a host cell.

Read the question and write your answers in the spaces provided.

SKILL: Interpreting Graphics

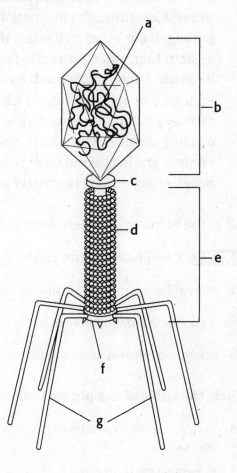

1. The figure on the right shows a bacteriophage. On the lettered lines to the side of the figure, write the label that describes the structure indicated by the corresponding letter on the figure. You will use the following labels: "Base plate," "Collar," "Head," "Nucleic acid," "Sheath," "Tail," and "Tail fibers."

   a. _____

   b. _____

   c. _____

   d. _____

   e. _____

   f. _____

   g. _____

Circle the letter of the phrase that best completes the statement.

2. The contractile tail of a bacteriophage helps the virus

   a. attach itself to a host cell.

   b. inject nucleic acid into the host cell.

   c. assemble new viruses.

   d. Both (a) and (b)

CHAPTER 24 ACTIVE READING WORKSHEETS

VIRUSES

Section 24-2: Viral Diseases

**Read the passage below, which covers topics from your textbook.
Answer the questions that follow.**

The control of viral diseases is accomplished in two ways: vacci-nation to prevent disease and administration of antiviral drugs—drugs that interfere with viral nucleic acid synthesis—to infected patients. Unfortunately, there are few antiviral drugs compared to drugs used to treat bacterial, fungal, and parasitic infections. The most successful approach to controlling viral diseases has been prevention through vaccination. A vaccine is a preparation of pathogens or other materials that stimulates the body's immune system to provide protection against that pathogen. Vaccines can be made from inactivated or attenuated viruses. **Inactivated** viruses can not replicate in a host system. **Attenuated** viruses are viruses that have been weakened so that they are incapable of causing disease. In general, vaccines made from attenuated viruses are preferred over those made from inactivated viruses because protection is greater and lasts longer.

Fill in the blank to complete each sentence.

SKILL: Completing Sentences

1. Antiviral drugs interfere with viral nucleic acid _____ .

2. A vaccine is a preparation of pathogens that stimulates the body's _____ .

3. Inactivated viruses cannot replicate in a _____ .

Circle the letter of the phrase that best completes the statement.

4. Vaccines made from attenuated viruses are preferred over those made from inactivated viruses because

   a. protection is greater.
   b. protection lasts longer.
   c. attenuated viruses are milder than inactivated viruses.
   d. Both (a) and (b)

PROTISTS

Section 25-1: Characteristics of Protists

Read the passage below, which covers topics from your textbook. Answer the questions that follow.

Protists come in a wide variety of body plans. Most protists are unicellular, such as amoebas and euglenoids. Some protists, such as *Volvox*, form colonies in which several cells are joined into a larger body. Some of these colonies have a division of labor; certain cells specialize in reproduction, and other cells specialize in obtaining energy. A few protists, such as brown and red algae, form large multicellular bodies. Some brown algae may grow to more than 60 m in length. These marine giants have specialized regions for reproduction, photosynthesis, and attachment to the ocean floor. However, these regions lack the cellular differentiation found in true tissues and organs.

Use the passage to complete the table below.

SKILL: Organizing Information

Body Plan	Examples
Unicellular	1. 2.
3.	*Volvox*
4.	Brown algae
	5.

Circle the letter of the word or phrase that best completes the sentence.

6. Specialized regions in multicellular protists are not true tissues and organs because

    a. they lack cellular differentiation.
    b. not all multicellular protists have them.
    c. they lack cells.
    d. their cells do not contain nuclei.

PROTISTS

Section 25-2: Animal-Like Protists

Observe the figure below, which covers topics from your textbook.
Answer the questions that follow.

A Summary of Animal-Like Protists				
Phylum	**Common name**	**Locomotion**	**Nutrition type**	**Representative genera**
Protozoa	sarcodines	pseudopodia	heterotrophic; some parasitic	Amoeba Radiolaria Entamoeba
Ciliophora	ciliates	cilia	heterotrophic; some parasitic	Paramecium Stentor Balantidium
Sarcomastigophora	mastigophorans	flagella	heterotrophic; some parasitic	Trypanosoma Leishmania Giardia Trichonympha
Apicomplexa	sporozoans	(none in adult)	heterotrophic; parasitic	Plasmodium Toxoplasma

Read each question and write your answer in the space provided.

SKILL: Organizing Information

1. Based on the entries in the column labeled "Nutrition type," how are all phyla of animal-like protists alike?

   _____

2. What is the common name of members of the phylum Ciliophora?

   _____

Circle the letter of the word that best completes the analogy.

3. Sarcomastigophora is to *Giardia* as Protozoa is to

   a. *Trypanosoma.*
   b. *Toxoplasma.*
   c. *Entamoeba.*
   d. *Balantidium.*

PROTISTS

Section 25-3: Plantlike and Funguslike Protists

Read the passage below, which covers topics from your textbook. Answer the questions that follow.

The phylum Euglenophyta contains approximately 1,000 species of flagellated unicellular algae called **euglenoids.** Euglenoids show both plantlike and animal-like characteristics. They are plantlike in that many have chlorophyll and are photosynthetic; they are animal-like in that they lack a cell wall and are highly motile. A familiar genus of euglenoids is *Euglena. Euglena* is abundant in fresh water, especially water polluted by excess nutrients. This protist has an elastic, transparent pellicle made of protein just beneath its cell membrane. It also has a contractile vacuole to rid the cell of excess water. Because *Euglena* lacks a cell wall, it is fairly flexible and can change its shape as it moves about. Although usually photosynthetic, if *Euglena* is raised in a dark environment, it will not form chloroplasts and will become heterotrophic.

Read each question and write your answer in the space provided.

SKILL: Recognizing Cause-and-Effect Relationships

1. What two traits of euglenoids cause them to be called plantlike?

_____

2. What two traits of euglenoids cause them to be called animal-like?

_____

Circle the letter of the phrase that best completes the statement.

3. Because *Euglena* lacks a cell wall, the protist can

 a. expel excess water.
 b. change shape as it moves.
 c. produce its own food.
 d. Both (a) and (b)

CHAPTER 25 ACTIVE READING WORKSHEETS

PROTISTS

Section 25-4: Protists and Humans

Read the passage below, which covers topics from your textbook. Answer the questions that follow.

The best-known sporozoan is *Plasmodium*, the protist that causes malaria. Four species of *Plasmodium* infect humans, and all have life cycles that involve the female *Anopheles* mosquito. When an infected mosquito bites a person, *Plasmodium* **sporozoites** enter the bloodstream and travel to liver cells, where they divide repeatedly. New cells called **merozoites** emerge and infect red blood cells, where they reproduce asexually. At regular intervals, the merozoites burst out of the red blood cells and release toxins into the blood. The merozoites infect other red blood cells and again reproduce asexually. Some of the merozoites in the blood develop into sexual cells called **gametocytes.** When a female *Anopheles* bites the infected person, it ingests these gametocytes. In the mosquito's digestive system, the sperm and eggs that form from the gametocytes combine to form a zygote. The nucleus of the zygote divides repeatedly to form more sporozoites. When the insect bites another person, the life cycle begins again.

Fill in the blank to complete the sentence.

SKILL: Completing Sentences

1. All four species of *Plasmodium* have life cycles that involve the female _____ .

Read the question and write your answer in the space provided.

SKILL: Vocabulary Development

2. What is the meaning of the term *intervals* in the passage?

_____

Circle the letter of the phrase that best completes the analogy.

3. Merozoites are to red blood cells as sporozoites are to

   a. liver cells.   **c.** the digestive system.

   b. a zygote.   **d.** Both (a) and (b)

FUNGI

Section 26-1: Overview of Fungi

Read the passage below, which covers topics from your textbook. Answer the questions that follow.

Fungi are eukaryotic, nonphotosynthetic organisms, and most are multicellular heterotrophs. Most fungi are microscopic molds or yeasts. **Molds,** such as the fungus that grows on bread and oranges, are tangled masses of filaments of cells. **Yeasts** are unicellular organisms whose colonies resemble those of bacteria.

Filaments of fungi are called **hyphae.** The cell walls of hyphae contain **chitin,** a complex polysaccharide not found in bacteria, protists, or other microorganisms but found in insects. The presence of chitin distinguishes cell walls of fungi from those of plants, which have cellulose but not chitin.

While animal and many microorganisms ingest their nutrients before digesting them, fungi secrete enzymes and then absorb the digested nutrients through their cell wall. Like animals, fungi store energy in the form of glycogen.

Read each question and write your answer in the space provided.

SKILL: Recognizing Similarities and Differences

One reading skill is the ability to recognize similarities and differences between phrases, ideas, or things.

1. How are molds and yeasts alike?

   _____

2. Suppose a specimen is found to contain glycogen. How might this specimen be classified?

   _____

Circle the letter of the word that best completes the statement.

3. The polysaccharide chitin is found in

   a. insects.
   b. fungi.
   c. bacteria.
   d. Both (a) and (b)

CHAPTER 26 ACTIVE READING WORKSHEETS

FUNGI

Section 26-2: Classification of Fungi

Read the passage below, which covers topics from your textbook. Answer the questions that follow.

A **mycorrhiza** is a symbiotic association between a fungus and plant roots. The fungus absorbs and concentrates phosphate and other ions for delivery to the plant root and increases surface area of the plant's root system. In turn, the fungi receives sugars synthesized by the plant during photosynthesis. All three fungal phyla form mycorrhizae. These mycorrhizal relationships are crucial for plant growth and development.

Lichens represent symbiotic relationships between a fungus and a photosynthetic partner (usually a cyanobacterium or green alga). Most fungi in lichens are ascomycetes. The photosynthesizer synthesizes sugars for the fungus, while the fungus provides moisture, shelter, and anchorage for the photosynthesizer. The fungus produces acids that decompose rocks making minerals available to the lichen. The chemical decomposition of rocks by lichens contributes to the production of soil.

Read each question and write your answer in the space provided.

SKILL: Identifying Main Ideas

The main idea is the main focus or key idea in a piece of written manuscript. Frequently a main idea is accompanied by supporting information that offers detailed facts about the main idea.

1. What is a mycorrhiza?

_____

2. What is a lichen?

_____

Circle the letter of the phrase that best completes the sentence.

3. Lichens aid soil production by

   a. synthesizing sugars.   **c.** decomposing rocks chemically.

   b. acting as a secondary root system.   **d.** Both (a) and (b)

FUNGI

Section 26-3: Fungi and Humans

**Read the passage below, which covers topics from your textbook.
Answer the questions that follow.**

Many fungi are valuable food sources for humans. Yeast is an important nutritional supplement because it contains vitamins, minerals, and other nutrients. Mushrooms are also an important food often found in grocery stores in the United States. In other parts of the world, people prize the taste of other fungi, such as truffles and morels. Truffles and morels are ascocarps found near the roots of trees.

Fungi not only can add value to food but also can take value away. Many fungi are important plant pathogens that attack grain or fruit. For example, wheat rust is a basidiomycete that attacks wheat grains.

Fungi also produce several chemical compounds that are important to the food-processing industry, such as citric and gluconic acids. Citric acid is used in soft drinks and candies. Gluconic acid is fed to chickens to enhance the hardness of shells.

Fill in the blank to complete each sentence.

SKILL: Completing Sentences

Complete the sentence by logically finishing the thought.

1. Three examples of fungi used as human food sources are _____.

2. Yeast is an important nutritional supplement because it contains _____

_____

3. Some fungi are plant pathogens that attack _____.

Circle the letter of the word or phrase that best completes the statement.

4. Wheat rust is a basidiomycete that attacks
   a. wheat grains.
   b. wheat roots.
   c. eggshells.
   d. Both (a) and (b)

THE IMPORTANCE OF PLANTS

Section 27-1: Plants and People

Read the passage below, which covers topics from your textbook. Answer the questions that follow.

Cereals are grasses that contain grains. Grains are the edible, dry fruits of a cereal, such as rice, wheat, corn, oats, sorghum, rye, and millet.

Root crops are roots or underground stems that are rich in carbohydrates. Root crops include potatoes, beets, carrots, and radishes.

Legumes are members of the pea family and bear protein-rich seeds in pods. Soybean is the most important legume crop because it is produced in the largest amount and has many important uses.

A **fruit** is the part of a flowering plant that usually contains seeds. Food derived from the leaves, stems, seeds, and roots of soft plants are often called **vegetables**. Most **nuts** have a hard outer layer and contain a dry, one-seed fruit. Nuts include almonds, walnuts, pecans, and hazelnuts.

Read each description. On the line beside each phrase, write which of the following food crops the phrase describes: cereals, vegetables, nuts, legumes, fruits, or root crops.

SKILL: **Organizing Information**

_____ 1. underground stems that are rich in carbohydrates

_____ 2. foods derived from leaves, stems, seeds, or roots of soft plants

_____ 3. grasses that contain grains

_____ 4. bear protein-rich seeds in pods

Circle the letter of the word that best completes the statement.

5. The edible, dry fruits of a cereal are called

   a. nuts.
   b. grains.
   c. pods.
   d. legumes.

Name _____ Class _____ Date _____

THE IMPORTANCE OF PLANTS

Section 27-2: Plants and the Environment

**Read the passage below, which covers topics from your textbook.
Answer the questions that follow.**

[1] The study of the interactions between plants and the environment is called **plant ecology**. [2] The most important interaction involves the ability of plants to capture solar energy through photosynthesis. [3] In photosynthesis, plants absorb carbon dioxide from the air, produce sugar and starch, and break apart water, releasing oxygen into the air. [4] Consumers use oxygen in aerobic respiration and produce carbon dioxide and water. [5] Organic compounds from plants provide consumers with energy, building blocks, and essential molecules like vitamins and fiber.

Read each question and write your answer in the space provided.

SKILL: Identifying Main Ideas

One reading skill is the ability to identify the main idea of a passage.

1. What is the main idea of the passage?

_____

_____

2. What supporting detail does Sentence 5 provide the reader?

_____

Read the question and write your answer in the space provided.

SKILL: Vocabulary Development

3. What is the meaning of the term *essential* in the passage?

_____

Circle the letter of the word or phrase that best completes the statement.

4. Through photosynthesis, plants produce

   a. starch.   **c.** carbon dioxide.

   b. sugar.   **d.** Both (a) and (b)

CHAPTER 28 ACTIVE READING WORKSHEETS

PLANT EVOLUTION AND CLASSIFICATION

Section 28-1: Overview of Plants

Read the passage below, which is covers topics from your textbook. Answer the questions that follow.

The 12 phyla of plants, formerly referred to as *divisions,* can be divided into two groups based on the presence of vascular tissue. The three phyla of **nonvascular plants** have neither true vascular tissue nor true roots, stems, or leaves. Most members of the nine phyla of **vascular plants** have vascular tissue and true roots, stems, and leaves.

Vascular plants can further be divided into two groups, seedless plants and seed plants. Seedless plants include the phylum of ferns and three phyla made up of plants closely associated with ferns. **Seed plants**—plants that produce seeds for reproduction—include four phyla of gymnosperms and one phylum of angiosperms. **Gymnosperms,** which include pine trees, produce seeds that are not enclosed in fruits. **Angiosperms,** also known as flowering plants, produce seeds in a protective fruit. Examples are apple and orange trees.

Read each question and write your answer in the space provided.

SKILL: Forming Analogies

An analogy identifies a similar relationship between different pairs of items.

1. Complete the following analogy: "Seed plants are to angiosperms as seedless plants are to

_____."

2. Complete the following analogy: "Orange tree is to angiosperm as pine tree is to _____

_____."

Circle the letter of the phrase that best completes the statement.

3. Apple and pine trees are alike in that both organisms

   a. produce seeds for reproduction.
   b. lack vascular tissue.
   c. produce seeds within a protective fruit.
   d. lack true roots.

PLANT EVOLUTION AND CLASSIFICATION

Section 28-2: Nonvascular Plants

Read the passage below, which covers topics from your textbook. Answer the questions that follow.

Bryophytes are mostly terrestrial and have an alternation-of-generations life cycle. Bryophytes are seedless, and they produce spores. Because they do not have vascular tissue, they are very small, usually 1–2 cm (less than 1 in.) in height.

Bryophytes need water to reproduce sexually because the sperm must swim through water to an egg. The asexual production of haploid spores does not require water.

Mosses are called *pioneer plants* because they are often the first species to inhabit a barren area. This is an important environmental function because mosses gradually accumulate inorganic and organic matter on the surface of rocks, creating a layer of soil in which other plants can grow. In areas devastated by fire, volcanic action, or human activity, pioneering mosses can help trigger the development of new biological communities. They also help prevent soil erosion by covering the soil surface and absorbing water.

Read each question and write your answer in the space provided.

SKILL: Recognizing Cause-and-Effect Relationships

1. What causes bryophytes to be small?

_____

2. What effect of mosses' ability to accumulate matter on rocks' surface is described in the passage?

_____

Circle the letter of the phrase that best completes the statement.

3. In areas devastated by fire, mosses can trigger the development of

   a. vascular tissue.
   b. new biological communities.
   c. new species.
   d. Both (a) and (b)

PLANT EVOLUTION AND CLASSIFICATION

Section 28-3: Vascular Plants

Look at the figure below, which covers topics from your textbook.
Answer the questions that follow.

Comparing Monocots and Dicots					
Plant type	**Embryos**	**Leaves**	**Stems**	**Flower parts**	**Examples**
Monocots	One cotyledon	Parallel venation	Scattered vascular bundles	Usually occur in threes	lilies, irises, orchids, palms, tulips, bananas, pineapples, onions, bamboo, coconut, wheat, corn, rice, oats, barley, sugarcane
Dicots	Two cotyledons	Net venation	Radially arranged vascular bundles	Usually occur in fours or fives	beans, lettuce, oaks, maples, elms, roses, carnations, cactuses, most broad-leaved forest trees

Use the figure to answer the following questions. Write your answers on the lines provided.

SKILL: Interpreting Graphics

1. What are the similarities and differences between monocot and dicot leaves?

   _____

   _____

2. What are the similarities and differences between monocot and dicot stems?

   _____

   _____

Circle the letter of the word that best completes the analogy.

3. Monocot is to bamboo as dicot is to

   a. rice.
   b. orchid.
   c. banana.
   d. carnation.

PLANT STRUCTURE AND FUNCTION

Section 29-1: Plant Cells and Tissues

Read the passage below, which covers topics from your textbook. Answer the questions that follow.

Plant growth originates mainly in **meristems**, regions where cells continuously divide. Most plants grow in length through **apical meristems** located at the tips of stems and roots. Some monocots have **intercalary meristems** located above the bases of leaves and stems. Intercalary meristems allow grass leaves to quickly re-grow after being grazed or mowed.

Gymnosperms and most dicots also have **lateral meristems,** which allow stems and roots to increase in diameter. Lateral meristems are located near the outside of stems and roots. There are two types of lateral meristems, the vascular cambium and the cork cambium. The **vascular cambium,** located between the xylem and phloem, produces additional vascular tissues. The **cork cambium,** located outside the phloem, produces cork. Cork cells replace the epidermis in wood stems and roots, protecting the plant. **Cork** cells are dead cells that provide protection and prevent water loss.

Read each question and write your answer in the space provided.

SKILL: Forming Analogies

An analogy identifies a similar relationship between different pairs of items.

1. Complete the following analogy: "Apical meristems are to length as lateral meristems are to

_____."

2. Complete the following analogy: "Vascular tissues are to vascular cambium as cork is to

_____."

Circle the letter of the phrase that best completes the statement.

3. All categories of meristems are similar in that all meristems are regions where cells

   a. continuously divide.
   b. absorb water.
   c. increase in width.
   d. Both (a) and (b)

PLANT STRUCTURE AND FUNCTION

Section 29-2: Roots

Read the passage below, which covers topics from your textbook. Answer the questions that follow.

The root tip is covered by a protective **root cap,** which covers the apical meristem. The root cap produces a slimy substance that functions like lubricating oil, allowing the root to move more easily through the soil as it grows. Cells that are crushed or knocked off the root cap as it moves through the soil are replaced by new cells produced in the apical meristem, where cells are continuously dividing. **Root hairs,** which are extensions of epidermal cells, increase the surface area of the root and thus increase the plant's ability to absorb water and mineral nutrients.

Write the effect of each action identified below in the space provided.

SKILL: Recognizing Cause-and-Effect Relationships

1. Because the root cap is covered with a slimy substance that acts like lubricating oil, the root

_____.

2. Because root hairs increase the surface area of the root, they increase the plant's

_____.

Read the question and write your answer in the space provided.

SKILL: Vocabulary Development

3. What is the meaning of the term *slimy* in the passage?

_____

Circle the letter of the word or phrase that best completes the statement.

4. Root hairs are extensions of

   a. the root cap.
   b. the apical meristem.
   c. epidermal cells.
   d. hyphae.

CHAPTER 29 ACTIVE READING WORKSHEETS

PLANT STRUCTURE AND FUNCTION

Section 29-3: Stems

Read the passage below, which covers topics from your textbook. Answer the questions that follow.

Carbohydrates, some plant hormones, and other organic compounds are transported in the phloem. The movement of carbohydrates occurs from where the carbohydrates are made or have been stored, called a **source,** to where they are stored or used, called a **sink.** Botanists use the term **translocation** to refer to the movement of carbohydrates through the plant.

Movement in the phloem is explained by the **pressure-flow hypothesis,** which states that carbohydrates are actively transported into sieve tubes. As carbohydrates enter the sieve tubes, water is also transported in by osmosis. Thus, a positive pressure builds up at the source end of the sieve tube.

At the sink end of the sieve tube, this process is reversed. Carbohydrates are actively transported out, water leaves the sieve tube by osmosis, and pressure is reduced at the sink. The difference in pressure causes water to flow from source to sink—carrying dissolved substances with it.

Fill in the blank to complete each sentence.

SKILL: Completing Sentences

1. The movement of carbohydrates through the plant is known as _____.

2. Water is transported into the sieve tube by _____.

Read the question and write your answer in the space provided.

SKILL: Vocabulary Development

3. Compare the use of the term *source* in the passage with its use in the reference section of a research paper.

    _____

    _____

    _____

continued on the next page . . .

Name _____ Class _____ Date _____

Write your answers in the spaces provided.

SKILL: Interpreting Graphics

4. The diagram below illustrates the pressure-flow model. Complete the figure by adding the following labels: "Phloem," "Sink," and "Source." For the blanks (d) and (e), identify the substance that is transported along the path of the respective arrow.

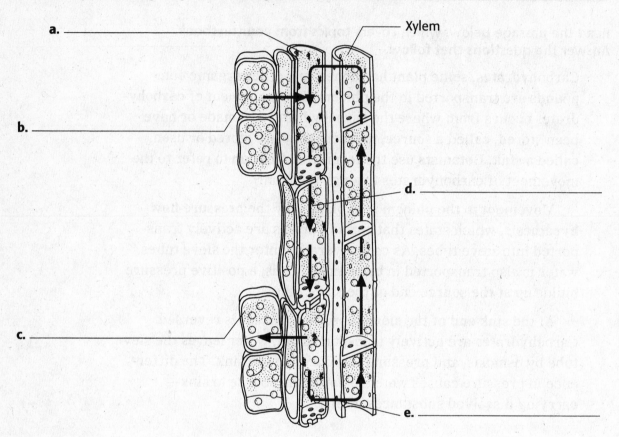

a. _____

Xylem

b. _____

d. _____

c. _____

e. _____

Circle the letter of the word or phrase that best completes the analogy.

5. Stored carbohydrates is to source as used carbohydrates is to

    a. translocation.

    b. sieve tube.

    c. xylem.

    d. sink.

PLANT STRUCTURE AND FUNCTION

Section 29-4: Leaves

Read the passage below, which covers topics from your textbook. Answer the questions that follow.

Leaves come in a wide variety of shapes and sizes and are an important feature used for plant identification. Leaves can be round, straplike, needlelike, or heart-shaped. The broad, flat portion of a leaf, called the **blade,** is the site of most photosynthesis. The blade is usually attached to the stem by a stalklike **petiole.** The maple leaf is a **simple leaf;** it has a single blade. In **compound leaves** such as the white clover, the blade is divided into **leaflets.** In some species, the leaflets themselves are divided. The result is a doubly compound leaf, such as that of the honeylocust.

Leaves consist of three tissue systems. The dermal tissue system is represented by the epidermis. In most leaves the epidermis is a single layer of cells coated with a nearly impermeable cuticle. Water, oxygen, and carbon dioxide enter and exit the leaf through stomata in the epidermis. Epidermal hairs are often present and usually function to protect the leaf from insects and intense light.

In most plants, photosynthesis occurs in the leaf **mesophyll,** a ground tissue composed of chloroplast-rich parenchyma cells. In most plants, the mesophyll is organized into layers. The **palisade mesophyll** layer occurs directly beneath the upper epidermis and is the site of most photosynthesis. Palisade cells are columnar and appear to be packed tightly together in one or two layers. However, there are air spaces between the long side walls of palisade cells. Beneath the palisade layer is the **spongy mesophyll.** It consists of irregularly shaped cells surrounded by large air spaces, which allow oxygen, carbon dioxide, and water to diffuse into and out of the leaf.

Read the question and write your answer in the space provided.

SKILL: Vocabulary Development

1. What is the meaning of the term *impermeable* in the passage?

_____

continued on the next page . . .

Name _____ Class _____ Date _____

Read each description related to leaves. On the line, write the term described.

_____ 2. the leaf's dermal tissue system

_____ 3. structure that attaches the blade to the stem

_____ 4. structure that consists of irregularly shaped cells
                                        surrounded by large air spaces

_____ 5. the broad, flat leaf part where most photosyn-
                                        thesis occurs

_____ 6. ground tissue made up of chloroplast-rich
                                        parenchyma cells

_____ 7. leaf with a single blade

_____ 8. the plant part whose columnar cells have air
                                        spaces between them

_____ 9. leaf with a divided blade

Write your answers in the spaces provided.

SKILL: Interpreting Graphics

10. The figure below shows the internal structure of a leaf. Write the following labels on the figure:
    "Spongy mesophyll," "Cuticle," "Palisade mesophyll," and "Upper epidermis." Write your answers
    on the lines provided.

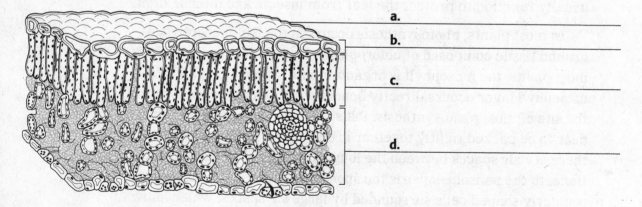

a. _____

b. _____

c. _____

d. _____

Circle the letter of the word or phrase that best completes the analogy.

11. Simple is to maple leaf as compound is to

    a. corn leaf.
    b. white clover.
    c. vein.
    d. Both (a) and (b)

PLANT REPRODUCTION

Section 30-1: Plant Life Cycles

**Read the passage below, which covers topics from your textbook.
Answer the questions that follow.**

In pines, sexual reproduction takes more than two years. During the first summer, a mature pine tree produces separate male and female cones. The male cones produce *microsporangia*, while the female cones produce *megasporangia*. The following spring, cells in all sporangia undergo meiosis and divide to produce haploid spores. *Megasporangia* produce megaspores, which develop into *megagametophytes*, or female gametophytes. A thick layer of cells called an **integument** surrounds each megasporangium. The integument has a small opening called the **micropyle.** Together, a megasporangium and its integument form a structure called an **ovule.** Two ovules develop on each scale of a female cone. *Microsporangia* produce microspores, which develop into *microgametophytes*, or male gametophytes. A **pollen grain** is a microgametophyte of a seed plant.

The male cones of a pine release huge numbers of pollen grains. Pine pollen travels on the wind, and only a few grains may land on a female cone. The pollen grains drift between the cone scales until they reach the ovules. The arrival of a pollen grain at the micropyle of a pine ovule is called pollination. A drop of fluid at the micropyle captures the pollen grain. As the fluid dries, the pollen grain is drawn into the micropyle. After pollination, the female gametophyte within the ovule produces archegonia and eggs.

After pollination, the pollen grain begins to grow a **pollen tube,** a slender extension of the pollen grain that enables sperm to reach an egg. When the pollen tube reaches an archegonium, one sperm unites with an egg to form a zygote. The other sperm and the pollen tube die. Over the next few months, the zygote develops into an embryo as the ovule matures into a seed.

Read the question and write your answer in the space provided.

SKILL: Vocabulary Development

1. Compare the meaning of the term *scale* in the passage with its meaning in a music class.

_____

_____

continued on the next page . . .

Name _____ Class _____ Date _____

Write your answers in the spaces provided.

SKILL: Organizing Information

2. The diagram below shows the life cycle of a gymnosperm. Complete the diagram by inserting the following labels: Ovule," "Megasporangium," "Meiosis," "Micropyle," "Microsporangium," "Pollen grain," "Pollen tube," "Seed," and "Fertilization." Some terms may be used more than once.

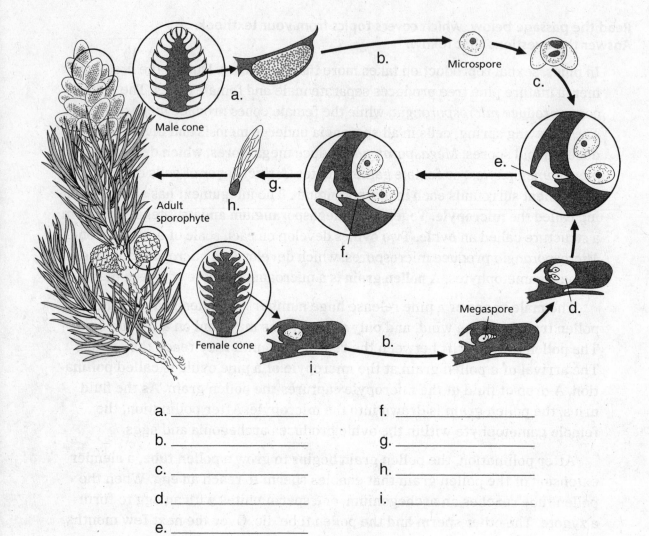

a. _____   f. _____

b. _____   g. _____

c. _____   h. _____

d. _____   i. _____

e. _____

Circle the letter of the word that best completes the analogy.

3. Female gametophytes are to megasporangia as male gametophytes are to

   a. integument.
   b. zygote.
   c. microsporangia.
   d. archegonia.

PLANT REPRODUCTION

Section 30-2: Sexual Reproduction in Flowering Plants

Read the passage below, which covers topics from your textbook. Answer the questions that follow.

Flower parts are usually found in four concentric whorls, or rings. **Sepals** make up the outermost whorl of flower parts. They surround and protect the other parts of a developing flower before it opens. **Petals** make up the next whorl. The petals and sepals of wind-pollinated plants are usually small or absent.

The two innermost whorls of flower parts contain the reproductive structures. The male reproductive structures are **stamens,** each of which consists of an anther and a filament. An **anther** contains microsporangia, which produce microspores that develop into pollen grains. A stalklike **filament** supports an anther. The innermost whorl contains the female reproductive structures, which are called **carpels.** One or more carpels fused together make up the structure called a **pistil.** The enlarged base of a pistil is called the **ovary.** A **style,** which is usually stalklike, rises from the ovary. The tip of the style is called the **stigma.** Generally, a stigma is sticky or has hairs, enabling it to trap pollen grains.

Read each description. Write the name of the flower part described on the line provided.

SKILL: Vocabulary Development

_____ 1. enlarged base of a pistil

_____ 2. structures that surround and protect parts of a developing flower

_____ 3. structure that traps pollen grains with its sticky surface

_____ 4. female reproductive structures

_____ 5. structure that contains microsporangia

_____ 6. male reproductive structures

continued on the next page . . .

Write you answers in the spaces provided.

SKILL: Interpreting Graphics

7. Insert the following labels on the diagram of a flower shown below: "Anther," "Filament," "Ovary," "Ovule," "Petal," "Pistil," "Sepal," "Stamen," "Stigma," and "Style."

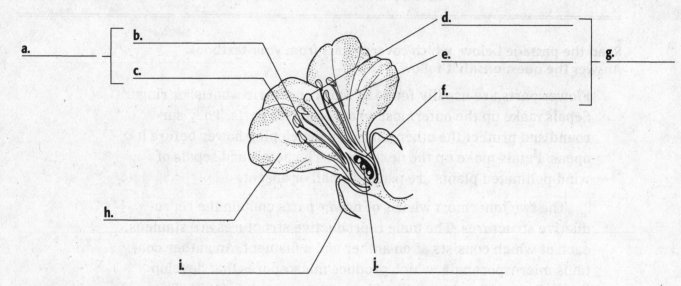

Read the question and write your answer in the space provided.

SKILL: Vocabulary Development

8. What is the meaning of the term *concentric* in the passage?

_____

Circle the letter of the word that best completes the statement.

9. A flower classified as a male flower lacks

    a. pistils.
    b. petals.
    c. sepals.
    d. Both (a) and (b)

Name _____ Class _____ Date _____

PLANT REPRODUCTION

Section 30-3: Dispersal and Propagation

**Read the passage below, which covers topics from your textbook.
Answer the questions that follow.**

Most of the interior of a bean seed is filled by two large, fleshy cotyledons (seed leaves), which are part of the embryo. Recall that angiosperms are classified as either monocots or dicots, based on the number of cotyledons in their embryos. Therefore, beans are dicots. A mature bean seed has no endosperm. The endosperm was absorbed by the fleshy cotyledons.

Between the two cotyledons of a bean seed are the parts that make up the rest of the embryo. The shoot tip, along with any embryonic leaves, is called the **plumule.** The **epicotyl** extends from the plumule to the attachment point of the cotyledons. The **hypocotyl** extends from the attachment point of the cotyledons to the radicle. The **radicle** is the embryonic root. Along the concave edge of the seed, beneath the radicle, is the **hilum,** which is a scar that marks where the seed was attached to the ovary wall.

Another type of seed is the corn kernel. Technically, a corn kernel is a fruit, but the seed occupies almost the entire kernel. The wall of the fruit is very thin and is fused to the seed coat. A single umbrella-shaped cotyledon is pressed close to the endosperm. The cotyledon of a monocot seed does not store nutrients, as bean cotyledons do. Instead, it absorbs nutrients from the endosperm and transfers them to the embryo.

Write your answers in the spaces provided.

SKILL: Interpreting Graphics

1. The diagram shows the structure of a bean seed. Complete the diagram by inserting the following labels: "Cotyledons," "Hypocotyl," "Radicle," "Plumule," and "Seed coat."

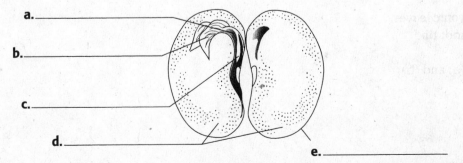

a. _____

b. _____

c. _____

d. _____

e. _____

continued on the next page . . .

Write the answer to each question on the line provided.

SKILL: Identifying Main Ideas

2. What are the similarities and differences between a bean seed and a kernel of corn?

_____

_____

_____

3. Why does a mature bean seed lack an endosperm?

_____

_____

4. What does the hilum of a seed indicate?

_____

_____

5. What is the function of a corn kernel's cotyledon?

_____

_____

Read the question and write your answer in the space provided.

SKILL: Vocabulary Development

6. What is the meaning of the term *concave* in the passage?

_____

_____

Circle the letter of the word or phrase that best completes the statement.

7. The plumule of a bean seed contains

   a. embryonic leaves.
   b. the shoot tip.
   c. hilum.
   d. Both (a) and (b)

CHAPTER 31 ACTIVE READING WORKSHEETS

PLANT RESPONSES

Section 31-1: Plant Hormones

Read the passage below, which covers topics from your textbook. Answer the questions that follow.

[1] Plant **hormones** are chemical messengers that affect a plant's ability to respond to its environment. [2] Hormones are organic compounds that are effective at very low concentrations; they are usually synthesized in one part of the plant and transported to another location. [3] They interact with specific target tissues to cause physiological responses, such as growth or fruit ripening. [4] Each response may be the result of two or more hormones acting together.

[5] Because hormones can stimulate or inhibit plant growth, many botanists also refer to them as plant **growth regulators**. [6] Many hormones can be synthesized in the laboratory, increasing the quantity of hormones available for commercial applications. [7] Botanists recognize five major groups of hormones: auxins, gibberellins, ethylene, cytokinins, and abscisic acid.

Read each question and write your answer in the space provided.

SKILL: Recognizing Text Structure

1. Text structure is the format an author uses to organize ideas. The author of this passage used a text structure consisting of a main idea and supporting details. What is the main idea of the passage?

   _____

   _____

2. What are the five major groups of hormones?

   _____

Circle the letter of the phrase that best completes the statement.

3. Hormones are organic compounds that are effective at very
   a. low concentrations.
   b. low temperatures.
   c. high concentrations.
   d. Both (a) and (b)

PLANT RESPONSES

Section 31-2: Plant Movements

Read the passage below, which covers topics from your textbook. Answer the questions that follow.

A **tropism** is a plant movement that is determined by the direction of an environmental stimulus. Movement toward an environmental stimulus is called a *positive* tropism, and movement away from a stimulus is called a *negative* tropism. Each kind of tropism shown in the table below is named for its stimulus.

Various Plant Tropisms		
Tropism	**Stimulus**	**Positive example**
Phototropism	light	plant leans toward light
Thigmotropism	contact with object	vine twines around a tree
Gravitropism	gravity	roots grow downward
Chemotropism	chemical	pollen tube grows toward ovule

Read each question and write your answer in the space provided.

SKILL: Forming Analogies

1. Complete the following analogy: "Light is to phototropism as contact is to _____

_____."

2. Complete the following analogy: "Chemotropism is to chemical as gravitropism is to _____

_____."

Read each question and write your answer in the space provided.

SKILL: Vocabulary Development

3. The prefix *photo-* means "light." Name three terms that contain this prefix.

_____

Circle the letter of the word that best completes the statement.

4. A vine that twines around a tree is a positive example of

   a. gravitropism.   **c.** thigmotropism.
   b. chemotropism.   **d.** phototropism.

CHAPTER 31 ACTIVE READING WORKSHEETS

PLANT RESPONSES

Section 31-3: Seasonal Responses

Read the passage below, which covers topics from your textbook. Answer the questions that follow.

Some tree leaves are noted for their spectacular fall color. The changing **fall colors** are caused mainly by a photoperiodic response but also by a temperature response. As night become longer in the fall, leaves stop producing chlorophyll. As the chlorophyll degrades, it is not replaced. Other leaf pigments, the carotenoids, become visible as the green chlorophyll degrades. Carotenoids include the orange carotenes and the yellow xanthophylls. The carotenoids were always in the leaf; they were just hidden by the more abundant chlorophyll. Another group of pigments found in leaves, the anthocyanins, are produced in cool, sunny weather. Anthocyanins produce beautiful red and purplish-red colors.

Read each question and write your answer in the space provided.

SKILL: Recognizing Text Structure

1. What type of text structure did the author use in the above passage?

_____

2. What are two causes of fall colors?

_____

Read the question and write your answer in the space provided.

SKILL: Vocabulary Development

3. What is the meaning of the term *degrades* in the passage?

_____

Circle the letter of the phrase that best completes the statement.

4. Most tree leaves appear green because green chlorophyll is

   a. a dominant trait.
   b. the only pigment a leaf contains.
   c. the most abundant leaf pigment.
   d. Both (a) and (b)

INTRODUCTION TO ANIMALS

Section 32-1: The Nature of Animals

**Read the passage below, which covers topics from your textbook.
Answer the questions that follow.**

The term **symmetry** refers to a body arrangement in which parts
that lie on opposite sides of an axis are identical. The simplest
animals, sponges, display no symmetry. Moreover, although
sponges are multicellular, their cells are not organized into tissues.
Animal bodies range from those that lack true tissues and an organized body shape, such as that of the sponge, to those that have very
organized tissues and a consistent body shape, as is found in most
other animal phyla.

Some animals have a top side and a bottom side, but no front,
back, right, or left end. These animals are said to display radial
symmetry. In **radial symmetry**, similar parts branch out in all
directions from a central line. Cnidarians, such as sea anemones,
jellyfish, and hydra, are radially symmetrical.

Most animals have a **dorsal** (back) and **ventral** (abdomen) side,
an **anterior** (head) and **posterior** (tail) end, and a right and left
side. Such animals have two similar halves on either side of a central plane and are said to display **bilateral symmetry.** Bilaterally
symmetrical animals tend to exhibit cephalization. **Cephalization**
is the concentration of sensory and brain structures in the anterior end of the animal; a cephalized animal has a head. As a
cephalized animal swims, burrows, walks, or flies through its environment, the head precedes the rest of the body, sensing danger,
prey, or a potential mate.

Read each question and write your answer in the space provided.

SKILL: Recognizing Text Structure

1. A writer will use different types of text structure to present organized ideas or events. The ability
to understand how ideas are organized will help you understand a text. What type of text structure did the author use in the above passage?

_____

continued on the next page . . .

2. How does the body structure of a sponge differ from that of a jellyfish?

_____

_____

3. What are the similarities and differences between radial symmetry and bilateral symmetry?

_____

_____

_____

_____

_____

4. Classify each of the drawings below as showing bilateral symmetry, no symmetry, or radial symmetry. Write your answers on the lines provided.

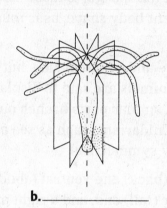
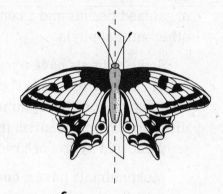

a. _____   b. _____   c. _____

Circle the letter of the phrase that best completes the statement.

5. An animal that exhibits cephalization

  a. has a head.
  b. usually is bilaterally symmetrical.
  c. lacks a brain.
  d. Both (a) and (b)

INTRODUCTION TO ANIMALS

Section 32-2: Invertebrates and Vertebrates

**Read the passage below, which covers topics from your textbook.
Answer the questions that follow.**

In most animals, the circulatory system moves blood or a similar
fluid through the body to transport oxygen and nutrients to cells.
At the same time, carbon dioxide and wastes are transported away
from the cells. Sponges and cnidarians have no circulatory system, so nutrients and gases are exchanged directly with the environment by diffusion across cell membranes. Arthropods and
some mollusks have an **open circulatory system,** in which bloodlike circulatory fluid is pumped from vessels in the body into the
body cavity, and then is returned to the vessels. Annelids and
other mollusks have a closed circulatory system. In a **closed circulatory system,** blood is pumped by a heart and circulates through
the body in vessels that form a closed loop. The exchange of gases,
nutrients, and wastes occurs between body cells and very small
blood vessels that lie near each cell.

Fill in the blank to complete each sentence.

SKILL: Completing Sentences

1. In most animals, the circulatory system moves blood or a similar fluid through the body to trans-

   port _____ to cells.

2. The circulatory system also moves _____ away from cells.

3. Because sponges lack a circulatory system, nutrients and gases are exchanged directly with the

   environment by _____.

4. In a(n) _____, bloodlike fluid is pumped from vessels in

   the body into the body cavity and then is returned to the vessels.

Circle the letter of the word that best answers the question.

5. Which of the following animals possess a closed circulatory system?

   a. sponges   **c.** annelids

   b. cnidarians   **d.** arthropods

CHAPTER 32 ACTIVE READING WORKSHEETS

INTRODUCTION TO ANIMALS

Section 32-3: Fertilization and Development

**Read the passage below, which covers topics from your textbook.
Answer the questions that follow.**

In most species, cleavage produces a raspberry-shaped mass of
16 to 64 cells. As the number of dividing cells further increases,
the mass becomes a hollow ball of cells called a **blastula.** Reorga-
nization of the cells of the hollow blastula begins with the inward
movement of cells at one end of the blastula. This process, called
gastrulation, transforms the blastula into a multilayered embryo,
called the **gastrula.** Gastrulation is marked by changes in the shape
of cells, together with changes in their adhesion to other cells.

As the inward folding continues, the now cup-shaped embryo
enlarges, and a deep cavity, called the **archenteron,** develops. The
open end of the archenteron is called the **blastopore**. Forming the
outer layer of the gastrula is the outer germ layer, the **ectoderm.**
The **endoderm** forms the inner germ layer of the gastrula. As
development progresses, a third layer, the **mesoderm,** forms
between the ectoderm and the endoderm.

Each of the three germ layers formed during gastrulation develops into certain organs in a process called *organogenesis*. The
endoderm forms the lining of the urinary system, the reproductive system, and most of the digestive tract; it also forms the pancreas, liver, lungs, and gills. The ectoderm forms the outer layer
of the skin, the hair, nails, and the nervous system. The mesoderm
forms a multitude of body parts, including the skeleton, muscles,
inner layer of the skin, circulatory system, and the lining of the
body cavity.

Read each question and write your answer in the space provided.

SKILL: Vocabulary Development

1. What is the meaning of the term *organogenesis* in this passage?

   _____

   _____

Identify the germ layer from which each part of the body forms. On the line, write "endoderm," "ectoderm," or "mesoderm."

SKILL: Organizing Information

_____ **2.** skeleton

_____ **3.** inner layer of the skin

_____ **4.** outer layer of the skin

_____ **5.** lungs

6. Complete the graphic organizer by adding the following terms: *blastula, endoderm, gastrula,* and *mesoderm.*

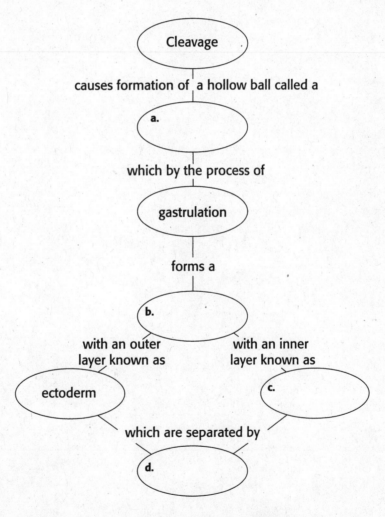

Circle the letter of the word that best completes the statement.

7. Through the process of gastrulation, a blastula is transformed into a multilayered

    a. blastocoel.

    b. zygote.

    c. embryo.

    d. archenteron.

SPONGES, CNIDARIANS, AND CTENOPHORES

Section 33-1: Porifera

Read the passage below, which covers topics from your textbook. Answer the questions that follow.

The basic body plan of a sponge consists of two layers of cells separated by a jellylike substance called *mesohyl*. In the simplest sponges, the body wall forms a hollow cylinder that is closed at the bottom and open at the top. The interior of the cylinder is lined with flagellated cells called **choanocytes.** By beating their flagella, choanocytes draw water into the sponge through numerous pores, called **ostia,** that penetrate the body wall. The water that is pumped into the interior of the sponge leaves through the **osculum,** the opening at the top of the sponge.

A sponge would collapse without some type of supporting structure. In some sponges, support is provided by a simple skeleton made of a network of protein fibers called **spongin.** Other sponges have skeletons consisting of **spicules,** tiny, hard particles of calcium carbonate or silicon dioxide. Still other sponges have a combination of spongin and spicules.

Read each question and write your answer in the space provided.

SKILL: Identifying Main Ideas

1. What is the main idea of the passage?

   _____

   _____

2. What is the basic body plan of a sponge?

   _____

   _____

continued on the next page . . .

3. How does water move into and out of a sponge?

_____

_____

_____

_____

4. The figure below shows the body plan of a sponge. Complete the figure by inserting the following labels: "Flagellum," " Choanocyte," "Spicules," "Osculum," "Interior of sponge," and "Ostium."

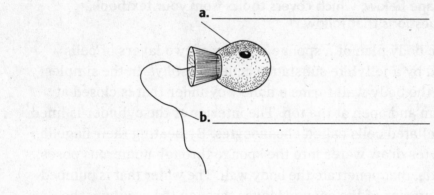

a. _____

b. _____

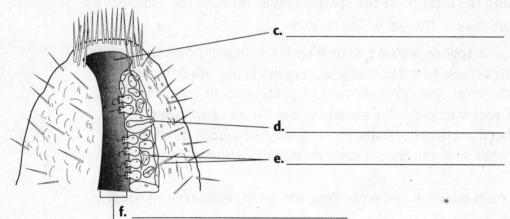

c. _____

d. _____

e. _____

f. _____

Circle the letter of the phrase that best completes the analogy.

5. Spicules are to sponge as

   a. sidewalk is to concrete.

   b. engine is to automobile.

   c. frame is to house.

   d. baseball is to bat.

SPONGES, CNIDARIANS, AND CTENOPHORES

Section 33-2: Cnidaria and Ctenophora

Read the passage below, which covers topics from your textbook. Answer the questions that follow.

Tiny freshwater hydra, stinging jellyfish, and flowerlike coral all belong to the phylum Cnidaria. Animals in this phylum are called *cnidarians*. The body of a cnidarian may be either bell-shaped or vase-shaped. The bell-shaped **medusa** is specialized for swimming. In contrast, the vase-shaped form, called a **polyp,** is specialized for a sessile existence.

All cnidarians have bodies constructed of two cell layers—an outer **epidermis** and an inner **gastrodermis.** Between these layers is a jellylike material known as **mesoglea.** In the center of the body is a hollow gut called the **gastrovascular cavity,** which has a single opening, or mouth. Surrounding the mouth are numerous flexible extensions called **tentacles.**

Read each question and write your answer in the space provided.

SKILL: Recognizing Similarities and Differences

1. How are all cnidarians alike?

_____

_____

2. What effect do the body plans of a polyp and a medusa have on movement?

_____

_____

_____

continued on the next page . . .

3. What body structures are common among cnidarians?

_____

_____

_____

4. The diagram shows the two body forms of cnidarians. Complete the diagram by inserting the following labels: "Epidermis," "Gastrodermis," "Gastrovascular cavity," "Medusa," "Mesoglea," "Mouth," "Polyp," and "Tentacle."

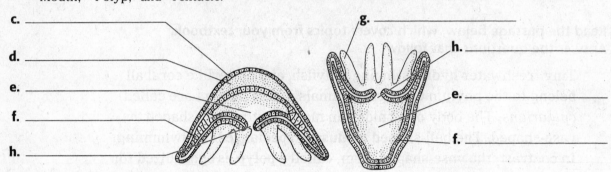

c. _____

d. _____

e. _____

f. _____

h. _____

g. _____

h. _____

e. _____

f. _____

a. _____   **b.** _____

Read the question and write your answer in the space provided.

SKILL: Vocabulary Development

5. What is the meaning of the term *sessile* in the passage?

_____

Circle the letter of the word that best completes the sentence.

6. All of the following are classified as cnidarians EXCEPT

   a. crayfish.

   b. hydra.

   c. jellyfish.

   d. coral.

FLATWORMS, ROUNDWORMS, AND ROTIFERS

Section 34-1: Platyhelminthes

Read the passage below, which covers topics from your textbook.
Answer the questions that follow.

Flukes have complicated life cycles. A good example is provided by the trematode blood flukes of the genus *Schistosoma*. Adult schistosomes live inside human blood vessels. Therefore, a human is the schistosome's **primary host,** the host from which the adult parasite gets its nourishment and in which sexual reproduction occurs. Unlike most flukes, schistosomes have separate sexes. Eggs produced by the female are fertilized by the male. Some of the fertilized eggs make their way to the host's intestine or bladder and are excreted with the feces or urine. Those that enter fresh water develop into ciliated larvae that swim. If the larvae encounter a snail of a particular species within a few hours, they burrow into the snail's tissues and begin to reproduce asexually. The snail serves as the schistosome's **intermediate host,** the host from which the larvae derive their nourishment. Eventually, the larvae develop tails and escape from the snail. These tailed larvae swim through the water. If they find the bare skin of a human, they penetrate the skin, enter a blood vessel, and develop into adults. At that point, the cycle begins again.

Write your answers in the spaces provided.

SKILL: Sequencing Information

1. Order the statements to show the life cycle of schistosomes. Write "1" on the line in front of the statement that describes what happens first. Write "2" on the line in front of the statement that describes what happens next, and so on.

_____ **a.** Tailed larvae leave the intermediate host.

_____ **b.** The fertilized eggs are excreted with feces or urine.

_____ **c.** The larvae enter a human blood vessel and develop into adults.

_____ **d.** The larvae burrow into a snail's tissues.

continued on the next page . . .

_____ **e.** The eggs are fertilized by a male.

_____ **f.** The larvae penetrate the skin of a new primary host.

_____ **g.** In a freshwater environment, the eggs develop into ciliated larvae.

_____ **h.** Once inside an intermediate host, the larvae reproduce asexually.

_____ **i.** An adult female schistosome releases eggs inside a primary host.

2. The figure illustrates the life cycle of an adult blood fluke. Insert the following labels on the diagram: "Ciliated larvae," "Egg," "Eggs," "Intermediate host," "Primary host," and "Tailed larva."

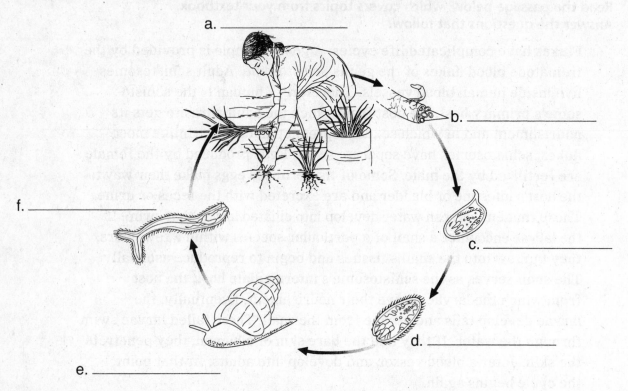

a. _____

b. _____

c. _____

d. _____

e. _____

f. _____

Read the question and write your answer in the space provided.

SKILL: Vocabulary Development

3. What is the meaning of the term *ciliated* in the passage?

_____

Circle the letter of the word or phrase that best completes the analogy.

4. In the life cycle of a blood fluke, primary host is to human as secondary host is to

    a. fresh water.
    b. tailed larva.
    c. snail.
    d. blood vessel.

FLATWORMS, ROUNDWORMS, AND ROTIFERS

Section 34-2: Nematoda and Rotifera

Read the passage below, which covers topics from your textbook. Answer the questions that follow.

One group of pseudocoelomates are the 1,750 species in the phylum Rotifera. Members of this phylum are called **rotifers.** Most rotifers are transparent, free-living animals that exist in fresh water, although some live in salt water and damp soil. Rotifers have a crown of cilia surrounding their mouth. Rotifers use the cilia to sweep food into their digestive tract. The food moves from the mouth to the **mastax,** a muscular organ that breaks the food into smaller particles. The food is further digested in the stomach, and the nutrients are absorbed in the intestine. Indigestible material passes from the intestine to the **cloaca,** a common chamber into which the digestive, reproductive, and excretory systems empty. Like planarians, rotifers use flame cells and excretory tubules to collect excess water in the body. The excess water, along with wastes from the intestine and eggs from the ovaries of females, leaves the cloaca through the anus. Rotifers exhibit cephalization, with a pair of cerebral ganglia and, in some species, two eyespots at the anterior end of the body.

Read the question and write your answer in the space provided.

SKILL: Vocabulary Development

1. What is the meaning of the term *crown* in the passage?

   _____

2. How is the mastax like your teeth?

   _____

continued on the next page . . .

Write your answer in the spaces provided.

SKILL: Interpreting Graphics

3. The diagram shows the anatomy of a rotifer. Complete the diagram by inserting the following labels: "Anus," "Cerebral ganglion," "Cilia," "Cloaca," "Excretory tubule," "Eyespot," "Flame cells," "Intestine," "Mastax," "Mouth," "Ovary," and "Stomach."

a. _____

b. _____

c. _____

d. _____

e. _____

f. _____

g. _____

h. _____

i. _____

j. _____

k. _____

l. _____

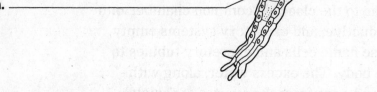

4. What is the function of the body structure labeled "j" in the figure?

_____

_____

5. What systems empty into the body structure labeled "l" in the figure?

_____

6. How do rotifers and planarians use the structures labeled "d" and "e"?

_____

_____

Circle the letter of the part of the diagram that best answers the question.

7. What part of the diagram shows the body structure that absorbs nutrients?

   a. a   **c.** g

   b. e   **d.** j

MOLLUSKS AND ANNELIDS

Section 35-1: Mollusca

Read the figure below, which covers topics from your textbook.
Answer the questions that follow.

Features of Three Classes of Mollusks				
Class	External shell	Head	Radula	Locomotion
Gastropoda	one (some species)	yes	yes	crawling (most)
Bivalvia	two	no	no	sessile (most)
Cephalopoda	none (most species)	yes	yes	rapid swimming

Read each question and write your answer in the space provided.

SKILL: Organizing Information

1. Based on the entries in the column labeled "External shell," how do bivalves differ from gastropods and cephalopods?

_____

_____

_____

2. What are two features that bivalves lack but gastropods and cephalopods possess?

_____

_____

Read the question and write your answer in the space provided.

SKILL: Vocabulary Development

3. What is the meaning of the term *locomotion* in the table?

_____

Circle the letter of the word that best completes the analogy.

4. Bivalvia is to sessile as Cephalopoda is to

   a. crawling.   **c.** jumping.

   b. swimming.   **d.** Both (a) and (b)

MOLLUSKS AND ANNELIDS

Section 35-2: Annelida

Read the passage below, which covers topics from your textbook. Answer the questions that follow.

An earthworm's body is divided into more than 100 segments, most of which are virtually identical. In addition, circular and longitudinal muscles line the interior body wall of an earthworm. To move, the worm anchors some of the middle segments by their setae and contracts the circular muscles in front of those segments. Contraction of the circular muscles increases the pressure of the coelomic fluid in those segments. This increased pressure elongates the animal and pushes the anterior end forward. Setae in the anterior segments then grip the ground as the longitudinal muscles contract, pulling the posterior segments forward. This method of locomotion in earthworms is an example of the kind of movement made possible by segmentation.

Read each question and write your answer in the space provided.

SKILL: Identifying Main Ideas

1. What is the main idea of this passage?

   _____

2. Describe the structure of an earthworm's body.

   _____

   _____

   _____

Circle the letter of the phrase that best completes the sentence.

3. As the earthworm's circular muscles contract, the

   a. organism's longitudinal muscles expand.
   b. pressure of the coelomic fluid decreases.
   c. organism's setae contract.
   d. pressure of the coelomic fluid increases.

ARTHROPODS

Section 36-1: Phylum Arthropoda

Read the passage below, which covers topics from your textbook. Answer the questions that follow.

A rigid exoskeleton limits the size to which an arthropod can grow. So, each arthropod periodically sheds its exoskeleton and makes a new one in the process of **molting.** An arthropod goes through many cycles of molting during its life.

A cycle of molting begins as the tissues of an arthropod gradually swell. When the pressure inside the exoskeleton is very strong, a hormone that triggers molting is produced. In response to this hormone, the cells of the epidermis secrete enzymes that digest the inner layer of the exoskeleton. At the same time, the epidermis begins to make a new exoskeleton by using the digested material. Eventually, the outer layer of the old exoskeleton loosens, breaks apart, and is shed. The new exoskeleton, which is flexible at first, stretches to fit the enlarged animal.

Read each question and write your answer in the space provided.

SKILL: Recognizing Cause-and-Effect Relationships

1. What causes an arthropod to produce a hormone that induces molting?

   _____

   _____

2. What two effects does the presence of this hormone have on the arthropod?

   _____

   _____

Circle the letter of the word or phrase that best completes the statement.

3. Each time an arthropod molts, the organism becomes

   a. better able to hide from predators.
   b. more adapted to its surroundings.
   c. larger.
   d. more flexible.

CHAPTER 36 ACTIVE READING WORKSHEETS

ARTHROPODS

Section 36-2: Subphylum Crustacea

Read the figure below, which covers topics from your textbook.
Answer the questions that follow.

Crayfish Appendages	
Appendage	**Function**
Antennule	touch, taste, balance
Antenna	touch, taste
Mandible	chew food
Maxilla	manipulate food, draw water currents over gills
Maxilliped	touch, taste, manipulate food
Cheliped	capture food, defense
Walking leg	locomotion over solid surfaces
Swimmeret	create water currents, transfer sperm (males)

Read each question and write your answer in the space provided.

SKILL: Forming Analogies

1. Complete the following analogy: "Locomotion is to walking leg as defense is to _____."

2. Complete the following analogy: "Antennule is to antenna as maxilla is to _____."

Circle the letter of the word that best completes the analogy.

3. Mandible is to chew as swimmeret is to

    a. defense.
    b. create water currents.
    c. balance.
    d. draw water over gills.

CHAPTER 36 ACTIVE READING WORKSHEETS

ARTHROPODS

Section 36-3: Subphyla Chelicerata and Myriapoda

Read the passage below, which covers topics from your textbook. Answer the questions that follow.

The nervous, digestive, and circulatory systems of spiders are similar to those of crustaceans. Because spiders are terrestrial, however, their respiratory system is quite different. In some spiders, respiration occurs in **book lungs,** paired sacs in the abdomen with many parallel folds that resemble the pages of a book. The folds in a book lung provide a large surface area for gas exchange. Other spiders have a system of tubes called **tracheae** that carry air directly to the tissues from openings in the exoskeleton known as **spiracles.** Some spiders have both book lungs and tracheae.

The excretory system of spiders is also modified for life on land. The main excretory organs, called **Malpighian tubules,** are hollow projections of the digestive tract that collect body fluids and wastes and carry them to the intestine. After most of the water is reabsorbed, the wastes leave the body in nearly solid form with the feces. Thus, the Malpighian tubules help spiders conserve water in terrestrial environments.

Fill in the blank to complete each sentence.

SKILL: Completing Sentences

1. The folds of a book lung provide a large surface area for _____ .

2. The respiratory system of a spider may contain both book lungs and _____

3. The main organs of the excretory system are the _____ .

Circle the letter of the phrase that best completes the analogy.

4. Book lungs are to respiratory system as Malpighian tubules are to

   a. digestive system.
   b. circulatory system.
   c. excretory system.
   d. Both (a) and (b)

Name _____ Class _____ Date _____

INSECTS

Section 37-1: The Insect World

Read the passage below, which covers topics from your textbook. Answer the questions that follow.

The body of a grasshopper clearly shows three tagmata. The most anterior tagma, the head, bears the mouthparts. It also has a pair of unbranched antennae as well as simple and compound eyes.

The middle tagma, the thorax, is divided into three parts: the prothorax, mesothorax, and metathorax. The *prothorax* attaches to the head and bears the first pair of walking legs. The *mesothorax* bears the forewings and the second pair of walking legs. The *metathorax* attaches to the abdomen and bears the hindwings and the large jumping legs.

Leathery forewings cover and protect the membranous hindwings when the grasshopper isn't flying.

The segments in the most posterior tagma, the abdomen, are composed of upper and lower plates that are joined by a tough but flexible sheet of exoskeleton. The exoskeleton is covered by a waxy cuticle that is secreted by the cells of the epidermis. The rigid exoskeleton supports the grasshopper's body, and the cuticle retards the loss of body water.

Read each description. On the line, write the name of the structure of the grasshopper's external anatomy described.

SKILL: Identifying Main Ideas

_____ 1. cover and protect the hindwings

_____ 2. part of the middle tagma that bears the forewings and walking legs

_____ 3. covered by a waxy cuticle

Circle the letter of the word or phrase that best completes the analogy.

4. Exoskeleton is to support as cuticle is to

   a. vision.   **c.** protection.

   b. water retention.   **d.** movement.

CHAPTER 37 ACTIVE READING WORKSHEETS

INSECTS

Section 37-2: Insect Behavior

Read the passage below, which covers topics from your textbook. Answer the questions that follow.

Some insects, such as certain species of bees, wasps, ants, and termites, live in complex colonies. In these colonies, some individuals gather food, others protect the colony, and others reproduce. Insects that live in such colonies are called **social insects.** The division of labor among social insects creates great interdependence and a heightened need for communication.

The behavioral adaptations of one type of social insect, the honeybee, are neither taught nor learned. Instead, they are genetically determined. Genetically determined behavior is called **innate behavior.**

A honeybee colony consists of three distinct types of individuals: worker bees, the queen bee, and drones. **Worker bees** are nonreproductive females that make up the vast majority of the hive population. The **queen bee** is the only reproductive female in the hive, and her only function is to reproduce. **Drones** are males that develop from unfertilized eggs. Their only function is to deliver sperm to the queen.

Read each question and write your answer in the space provided.

SKILL: Identifying Main Ideas

1. What is an innate behavior?

_____

_____

2. What are the three classes of individuals that make up a honeybee colony?

_____

_____

Circle the letter of the phrase that best completes the sentence.

3. The queen bee of a honeybee colony differs from other members in that she

  a. is the only reproductive female in the colony.
  b. gathers food for the drones.
  c. protects other members of the colony.
  d. is the only nonreproductive female in the colony.

ECHINODERMS AND INVERTEBRATE CHORDATES

Section 38-1: Echinoderms

Read the passage below, which covers topics from your textbook.
Answer the questions that follow.

The water-vascular system is a network of water-filled canals that are connected to the tube feet. Water enters the system through small pores in the **madreporite,** a sievelike plate on the aboral surface. Water then passes down the **stone canal,** a tube that connects the madreporite to the **ring canal,** which encircles the mouth. Another tube, the **radial canal,** extends from the ring canal to the end of each arm. The radial canals carry water to the hundreds of hollow tube feet. Valves prevent water from flowing back into the radial canals from the tube feet.

The upper end of each tube foot is expanded to form a bulblike sac called an **ampulla.** Contraction of muscles surrounding the ampullae forces water into the tube feet, causing them to extend. Contraction of muscles lining the tube feet forces water back into the ampullae and shortens the tube feet. In this way, the sea star uses water pressure to extend and withdraw its tube feet.

Write your answers in the spaces provided.

SKILL: Sequencing Information

1. Order the statements to show the steps of the water-vascular system of a sea star. Write "1" on the line in front of the statement that describes what happens first. Write "2" on the line in front of the statement that describes what happens next, and so on.

_____ **a.** The ring canal becomes filled with water.

_____ **b.** The tube feet extend.

_____ **c.** Water moves through the madreporite.

_____ **d.** Muscles lining the tube feet contract.

_____ **e.** Radial canals carry the water to hundreds of hollow tube feet.

_____ **f.** Water moves down the stone canal.

continued on the next page . . .

_____ g. Water is forced into the tube feet.

_____ h. Each tube foot expands to form an ampulla.

Write the answer to each question on the line provided.

SKILL: Identifying Main Ideas

2. What is the madreporite?

_____

3. What prevents water from flowing from the tube feet into the radial canals?

_____

4. While observing a sea star, you notice that its tube feet suddenly shorten. What can you infer has occurred within the echinoderm?

_____

_____

Read the question and write your answer in the space provided.

SKILL: Vocabulary Development

5. Compare the meaning of the term *feet* in the passage with its meaning in the sentence "Jon is over six feet tall."

_____

_____

_____

Circle the letter of the word that best completes the statement.

6. The water-vascular system facilitates

   a. respiration.
   b. movement.
   c. digestion.
   d. reproduction.

Name _____ Class _____ Date _____

ECHINODERMS AND INVERTEBRATE CHORDATES

Section 38-2: Invertebrate Chordates

Read the passage below, which covers topics from your textbook. Answer the questions that follow.

[1] In addition to a notochord, all chordates have the following characteristics during some stage of their life: a dorsal nerve cord, pharyngeal pouches, and a postanal tail. [2] Unlike the ventral nerve cords of invertebrates such as annelids and arthropods, the dorsal nerve cord of a chordate is a hollow tube. [3] In vertebrates, the anterior end of the nerve cord enlarges during development to form the brain, and the posterior end forms the spinal cord. [4] The brain receives information from a variety of complex sensory organs, many of which are concentrated at the anterior end of the body. [5] The pharyngeal pouches are outside pockets in the pharynx, the portion of the digestive tract between the mouth and the esophagus. [6] In aquatic chordates, the pharyngeal pouches became perforated by slits and evolved first into filter-feeding structures and later into gill chambers. [7] In terrestrial chordates, the pouches evolved into a variety of structures, including the jaws and inner ear. [8] The notochord or backbone extends into the postanal tail, and muscles in the tail can cause it to bend. [9] The postanal tail provides much of the propulsion in many aquatic chordates. [10] Invertebrates in other phyla lack this form of propulsion, because the anus, if present, is located at the end of the body.

Read each question and write your answer in the space provided.

SKILL: Recognizing Text Structure

1. What text structure did the author use in this passage?

_____

2. What does Sentence 5 describe to the reader?

_____

_____

continued on the next page . . .

3. In Sentences 6 and 7, what trait of aquatic chordates and terrestrial chordates is shown to differ?

_____

_____

_____

4. According to Sentences 6 and 7, how are the gill chambers of aquatic chordates similar to the inner ear of terrestrial chordates?

_____

_____

Write your answers in the spaces provided.

SKILL: Interpreting Graphics

5. The diagram shows structures common to all chordates. Complete the diagram by inserting the following labels: "Dorsal nerve cord," "Postanal tail," "Notochord," and "Pharyngeal pouch."

a. _____

b. _____

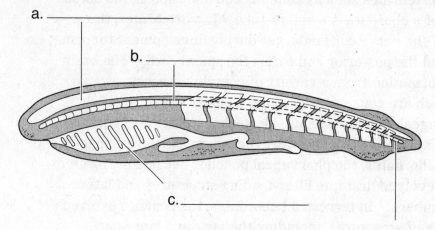

c. _____

d. _____

Read the question and write your answer in the space provided.

SKILL: Vocabulary Development

6. What is the meaning of the term *perforated* in the passage?

_____

_____

Circle the letter of the word that best completes the analogy.

7. In reference to the vertebrate nerve cord, posterior is to spinal cord as anterior is to

    a. esophagus.

    b. mouth.

    c. brain.

    d. Both (a) and (b)

CHAPTER 39 ACTIVE READING WORKSHEETS

FISHES

Section 39-1: Introduction to Vertebrates

Read the passage below, which covers topics from your textbook. Answer the questions that follow.

Vertebrates are one subphylum within the phylum Chordata. Like other chordates, vertebrates have, at some stage of their life, a notochord, a dorsal hollow nerve cord, pharyngeal pouches, and a post-anal tail. Vertebrates are a distinct group because they have three characteristics that distinguish them from other chordates. First, vertebrates have **vertebrae,** bones or cartilage that surrounds and protects the dorsal nerve cord. The vertebrae form the vertebral column, or spine. Second, vertebrates have a **cranium,** or skull, that protects the brain. Third, all vertebrates have an endoskeleton composed of bone or cartilage.

Read each question and write your answer in the space provided.

SKILL: Identifying Main Ideas

1. What is the main idea of the passage?

   _____

2. What three characteristics distinguish vertebrates from other chordates?

   _____

   _____

   _____

3. What structure do vertebrates have that protects their brain? _____

Circle the letter of the phrase that best completes the sentence.

4. At some stage of their lives, all vertebrates have

   a. pharyngeal pouches and a hollow nerve cord.
   b. a notochord and post-anal tail.
   c. undeveloped fins.
   d. Both (a) and (b)

FISHES

Section 39-2: Jawless and Cartilaginous Fishes

Read the passage below, which covers topics from your textbook. Answer the questions that follow.

¹ Cartilaginous fishes differ from jawless fishes in that fertilization occurs inside the body of the female. ² This type of fertilization is called **internal fertilization.** ³ During mating, the male transfers sperm into the female's body with modified pelvic fins called **claspers.** ⁴ In a few species of sharks and rays, the females lay large yolky eggs right after fertilization. ⁵ The young develop within the egg, are nourished by the yolk, and hatch as miniature versions of the adults. ⁶ The eggs of many species develop in the female's body, and the young are born live. ⁷ In some of these species, the mother nourishes the developing sharks while they are in her body. ⁸ No cartilaginous fishes provide parental care for their young after birth or hatching.

Read each question and write your answer in the space provided.

SKILL: Recognizing Text Structure

1. When items are compared, similarities between them are noted. When items are contrasted, dissimilarities or differences are noted. What trait of cartilaginous and jawless fishes is being contrasted in Sentence 1?

   _____

2. What is the similarity or difference of cartilaginous fishes identified in Sentence 8?

   _____

Circle the letter of the phrase that best completes the sentence.

3. In some species of cartilaginous fishes, the mother nourishes her developing sharks

   a. after they hatch from eggs.
   b. after they are born live.
   c. while they are inside her body.
   d. Both (a) and (b)

Name _____ Class _____ Date _____

FISHES

Section 39-3: Bony Fishes

Read the passage below, which covers topics from your textbook.
Answer the questions that follow.

The heart of a bony fish has two chambers in a row. Deoxygenated blood from the body first enters the sinus venosus. Next, blood moves into the first chamber, the atrium. Contraction of the atrium speeds up the blood and drives it into the muscular ventricle, the main pumping chamber of the heart. Contraction of the ventricle provides most of the force that drives the blood through the circulatory system. Blood then enters the conus arteriosus, a thickened, muscular part of the main artery leaving the heart. The conus arteriosus has an elastic wall and usually contains valves to prevent blood from flowing back into the ventricle. The conus arteriosus smooths the flow of blood from the heart.

Write your answers in the spaces provided.

SKILL: Interpreting Graphics

1. The diagram below illustrates the flow of blood through a fish's heart. Complete the diagram by adding the following labels: "Atrium," "Blood flow from the body," "Blood flow to the gills," "Conus arteriosus," "Sinus venosus," and "Ventricle."

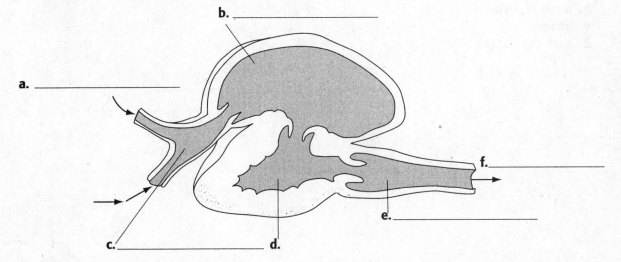

b. _____

a. _____

f. _____

c. _____ d. e. _____

continued on the next page . . .

Read each question and write your answer in the space provided.

SKILL: Sequencing Information

2. Order the statements to show how blood flows through a fish's heart. Write "1" on the line in front of the statement that describes what happens first. Write "2" on the line in front of the statement that describes what happens next, and so on.

_____ **a.** The blood moves into the atrium.

_____ **b.** Blood flows through the conus arteriosus.

_____ **c.** Blood is driven into the ventricle.

_____ **d.** Deoxygenated blood empties into the sinus venosus.

_____ **e.** The ventricle contracts.

_____ **f.** The atrium contracts.

Read the question and write your answer in the space provided.

SKILL: Vocabulary Development

3. What is the meaning of the term *chamber* in the passage?

_____

Circle the letter of the word or phrase that best completes the sentence.

4. Most of the force used to drive blood through a fish's circulatory system comes from the actions of the

   a. ventricle.
   b. sinus venosus.
   c. atrium.
   d. Both (a) and (b)

AMPHIBIANS

Section 40-1: Origin and Evolution of Amphibians

Read the passage below, which covers topics from your textbook. Answer the questions that follow.

Amphibians and lobe-finned fish share many anatomical similarities, including features of the skull and vertebral column. Also, the bones in the fin of a lobe-finned fish are similar in shape and position to the bones in the limb of an amphibian.

The oldest known amphibian fossils date from about 360 million years ago. All of the early amphibians had four strong limbs, which evolved from the fins of their fish ancestors. The forelimbs of amphibians (and all other terrestrial vertebrates) are homologous to the pectoral fins of fishes, and the hind limbs are homologous to the pelvic fins. The early amphibians also breathed air with lungs.

Read each question and write your answer in the space provided.

SKILL: Recognizing Text Structure

1. What text structure did the author use in the above passage?

_____

2. What trait did all early amphibians share?

_____

3. How are the forelimbs of amphibians and all other terrestrial vertebrates alike?

_____

Circle the letter of the word or phrase that best completes the sentence.

4. Amphibians and lobe-finned fish have similar

    a. predatory behaviors.
    b. skeletal features.
    c. lung structure.
    d. All of the above

CHAPTER 40 ACTIVE READING WORKSHEETS

AMPHIBIANS

Section 40-2: Characteristics of Amphibians

**Read the passage below, which covers topics from your textbook.
Answer the questions that follow.**

The amphibian digestive system includes the pharynx, esophagus, stomach, liver, gallbladder, small intestine, large intestine, and cloaca. The elastic esophagus and stomach allow an amphibian to swallow large amounts of food. Once food reaches the stomach, tiny glands in the stomach walls secrete gastric juices that help break down, or digest, the food. A muscle called the pyloric sphincter at the lower end of the stomach relaxes, which allows digested food to move into the small intestine. The upper portion of the small intestine is called the **duodenum.** The coiled middle portion of the small intestine is the **ileum.** A membrane resembling plastic wrap, called the **mesentery,** holds the small intestine in place. Inside the small intestine, digestion is completed and the released nutrients pass through capillary walls into the bloodstream, which carries them to all parts of the body.

The lower end of the small intestine leads into the large intestine. Here indigestible wastes are collected and pushed by muscle action into a cavity called the cloaca. Waste from the kidneys and urinary bladder, as well as either eggs or sperm from the gonads, also passes into the cloaca. Waste materials exit the body through the **vent.**

Write the name of digestive organ described on the line provided.

SKILL: Vocabulary Development

_____   1. where waste materials exit the body

_____   2. where digestion is completed

_____   3. the organ in which glands in the walls secrete gastric juices

_____   4. where indigestible materials are collected after leaving the small intestine

_____   5. holds the small intestine in place

_____   6. the organ into which eggs or sperm from the gonads may pass

Write your answers in the spaces provided.

SKILL: Interpreting Graphics

7. The diagram below illustrates the digestive system of a frog. Complete the diagram by adding the following labels: "Cloaca," "Duodenum," "Esophagus," "Ileum," "Large intestine," "Mesentery," "Mouth," "Stomach," "Pyloric sphincter," "Small intestine," and "Vent."

a. _____   b. _____

c. _____

d. _____

e. _____

f. _____

g. _____

h. _____

i. _____

j. _____

k. _____

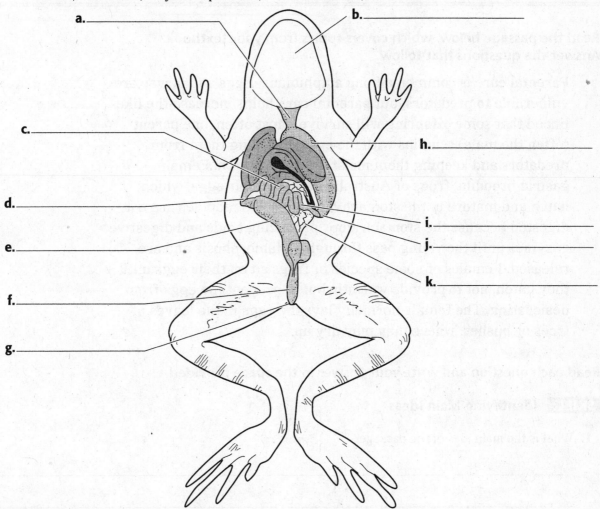

Read the question and write your answer in the space provided.

SKILL: Vocabulary Development

8. The prefix *in-* often means "not," while the suffix *-ible* means "able to do or make." How does knowledge of these word parts aid in decoding the term *indigestible*?

_____

_____

Circle the letter of the word or phrase that best completes the analogy.

9. Small intestine is to duodenum as stomach is to

   a. pyloric sphincter.   c. esophagus.
   b. vent.   d. cloaca.

CHAPTER 40 ACTIVE READING WORKSHEETS

AMPHIBIANS

Section 40-3: Reproduction in Amphibians

Read the passage below, which covers topics from your textbook. Answer the questions that follow.

Parental care is common among amphibians. Eggs and larvae are vulnerable to predators, but parental care helps increase the likelihood that some offspring will survive. Most often, one parent (often the male) remains with the eggs, guarding them from predators and keeping them moist until they hatch. Female gastric-brooding frogs of Australia swallow their eggs, which hatch and mature in the stomach. The eggs and tadpoles are not digested because the stomach stops producing acids and digestive enzymes until the young pass through metamorphosis and are released. Females of some species of frogs sit on their eggs until they hatch, not to provide warmth, but to prevent the eggs from desiccating. The female normally lays the eggs in the leaves of trees or bushes, where they may dry up.

Read each question and write your answer in the space provided.

SKILL: Identifying Main Ideas

1. What is the main idea of the passage?

   _____

   _____

2. Why do females of some species of frogs sit on their eggs until they hatch?

   _____

Circle the letter of the phrase that best completes the sentence.

3. The eggs and tadpoles of gastric-brooding frogs are not digested in the female parent's stomach because of a

   a. protective shell.
   b. halt in production of acids and digestive enzymes.
   c. lack of food needing to be digested.
   d. Both (a) and (b)

CHAPTER 41 ACTIVE READING WORKSHEETS

REPTILES

Section 41-1: Origin and Evolution of Reptiles

Read the passage below, which covers topics from your textbook. Answer the questions that follow.

> Until recently, most scientists thought that a single catastrophic event was responsible for the mass extinction of the dinosaurs. The **asteroid-impact hypothesis** suggest that a huge asteroid hit the Earth, sending so much dust into the atmosphere that the amount of sunlight reaching the Earth's surface was greatly reduced. The reduced sunlight caused severe climatic changes that led to the mass extinction. According to this hypothesis, the dinosaurs would have become extinct very quickly.

Read each question and write your answer in the space provided.

SKILL: Recognizing Text Structure

1. The author of this passage used a cause-and-effect text structure. In a cause-and-effect relationship, the cause is what makes something happen. The effect is the result of something and can be an event, decision, or situation. What cause-and-effect relationship does the passage explore?

   _____

   _____

2. According to the passage, what effect would an asteroid striking the Earth have on the atmosphere?

   _____

   _____

Circle the letter of the phrase that best completes the statement.

3. According to the asteroid-impact hypothesis, dinosaurs became extinct

   a. gradually over a decade.
   b. at the same time as other reptiles.
   c. very quickly.
   d. because of reproduction difficulties.

Name _____ Class _____ Date _____

REPTILES

Section 41-2: Characteristics of Reptiles

Read the passage below, which covers topics from your textbook. Answer the questions that follow.

There are three patterns of reproduction among reptiles. The differences between these three patterns lie in how long the eggs remain within the female and in how she provides them with nutrition.

In **oviparity,** the female's reproductive tract encloses each egg in a tough protective shell. The female then deposits the eggs in a favorable place in the environment. Oviparity is a characteristic of most reptiles, all birds, and three species of mammals.

One way to protect delicate eggs is to retain the eggs within the female's body for a time. This strategy is called **ovoviviparity.** The eggs may be laid shortly before hatching, or they may hatch within the female's body. The eggs absorb water and oxygen from the female, but they receive no nutrition other than the yolk.

In **viviparity,** a shell does not form around the egg, and the young are retained within the female's body until they are mature enough to be born. Nutrients and oxygen are transferred from mother to embryo through a structure called the **placenta.** The placenta forms from the membranes within the egg, and it brings blood vessels from the embryo near the vessels of the mother. Viviparity is the reproductive pattern shown by most mammals, but it is also found in a few species of lizards and snakes.

Read each question and write your answer in the space provided.

SKILL: Recognizing Similarities and Differences

1. What differences exist between the three patterns of reproduction described in this passage?

_____

_____

_____

2. How do eggs produced by oviparity and viviparity differ?

_____

_____

_____

3. What structure is unique to the reproduction pattern called viviparity?

_____

4. Which two reproductive patterns include retaining eggs within a female's body?

_____

Identify the pattern of reproduction associated with each description. Write "oviparity," "ovoviviparity," or "viviparity" on the line.

_____ **5.** The yolk supplies all nutrition.

_____ **6.** This reproductive pattern is found in a few species of snakes and lizards.

_____ **7.** Eggs are deposited in the environment.

_____ **8.** Eggs may hatch within the female's body.

_____ **9.** It is a trait of all birds.

_____ **10.** Eggs lack a shell.

Read the question and write your answer in the space provided.

SKILL: Vocabulary Development

11. The term *retained* comes from two Latin words meaning "to hold back." How is the term *retained* related to its words of origin?

_____

_____

Circle the letter of the word that best completes the analogy.

12. Viviparity is to most mammals as oviparity is to most

    a. amphibians.
    b. reptiles.
    c. humans.
    d. Both (a) and (b)

REPTILES

Section 41-3: Modern Reptiles

**Read the passage below, which covers topics from your textbook.
Answer the questions that follow.**

The order Squamata consists of about 5,500 species of lizards and snakes. A distinguishing characteristic of this order is an upper jaw that is loosely joined to the skull. Squamates are the most structurally diverse of the living reptiles, and they are found worldwide.

There are about 3,000 species of living lizards. Most lizards rely on agility, speed, and camouflage to elude predators. If threatened by a predator, some lizards have the ability to detach their tail. This ability is called **autotomy.** The tail continues to twitch and squirm after it detaches, drawing the predator's attention while the lizard escapes. The lizard grows a new tail in several weeks to several months, depending on the species.

Read each question and write your answer in the space provided.

SKILL: Identifying Main Ideas

1. To what order do lizards and snakes belong?

   _____

2. What distinguishing trait do members of this order possess?

   _____

3. What are three devices most lizards use to avoid predators?

   _____

Circle the letter of the phrase that best completes the sentence.

4. A lizard that loses its tail through autotomy

   a. can grow a new tail within a year.
   b. loses its ability to move.
   c. cannot reproduce.
   d. remains tail-less for the rest of its life.

BIRDS

Section 42-1: Origin and Evolution of Birds

Read the passage below, which covers topics from your textbook. Answer the questions that follow.

The evolution of a flying animal from nonflying ancestors entails many changes in anatomy, physiology, and behavior. According to one hypothesis, the ancestors of birds were tree dwellers that ran along branches and occasionally jumped between branches and trees. Wings that allowed these animals to glide from tree to tree evolved. Once gliding was possible, the ability to fly by flapping the wings evolved. Another hypothesis draws on the fact that the dinosaurs most closely related to birds were terrestrial and states that the evolution of birds must have occurred on the ground, not in the trees. Wings may have originally served to stabilize the animals as they leapt after prey. Or they may have been used for trapping or knocking down insect prey. Over generations, the wings became large enough to allow the animal to become airborne.

Fill in the blank to complete each sentence.

SKILL: **Completing Sentences**

1. The evolution of flying animals from nonflying ancestors involved changes in _____

   _____.

2. One hypothesis for the evolution of flight states that _____ evolved in tree-dwelling animals and allowed the animals to glide among trees.

3. A second hypothesis focuses on the fact that the dinosaurs most closely related to birds were

   _____.

4. Wings may have originally served to stabilize an animal as it _____.

Circle the letter of the phrase that best completes the sentence.

5. It is possible that wings may have been used to
   a. defend against predators.
   b. aid in movement along the ground.
   c. trap prey.
   d. Both (a) and (b)

CHAPTER 42 ACTIVE READING WORKSHEETS

BIRDS

Section 42-2: Characteristics of Birds

Read the passage below, which covers topics from your textbook. Answer the questions that follow.

The high metabolic rate of birds requires large amounts of oxygen. Yet some birds migrate thousands of miles at altitudes as high as 7,000 m (23,000 ft), where oxygen levels are very low. An elaborate and highly efficient respiratory system meets these oxygen needs. Air enters the bird's body through paired nostrils located near the base of the beak. The air passes down the trachea and enters two primary bronchi. From the bronchi, some of the air moves to the lungs. However, about 75 percent of the air bypasses the lungs and flows directly to the posterior air sacs. Nine sacs extend from the lungs, in most birds, occupying a large portion of the bird's chest and abdominal cavity. These sacs also extend into some of the long bones. Thus, the air sacs not only function in respiration but also greatly reduce the bird's density.

Gas exchange does not occur in the air sacs. Their function is to store air. When the bird exhales, the oxygen-poor air from its lungs is forced into the anterior air sacs, and the oxygen-rich air in the posterior air sacs is forced into the lungs. This way, the bird has oxygenated air in its lungs during both inhalation and exhalation.

Read each question and write your answer in the space provided.

SKILL: **Sequencing Information**

1. Order the statements to show the path air takes as it moves through a bird's respiratory system. Write "1" on the line in front of the statement that describes what happens first. Write "2" on the line in front of the statement that describes what happens next, and so on.

_____ **a.** The oxygen-rich air enters the lungs.

_____ **b.** About 75 percent of the air moves into the posterior air sacs.

_____ **c.** Air enters the bird's body through the nostrils.

_____ **d.** When the bird exhales, air leaves the posterior air sacs.

_____ **e.** The air moves through the trachea to the bronchi.

Read the question and write your answer in the space provided.

SKILL: Vocabulary Development

2. The term *posterior* is derived from a Latin word meaning "to come after." How does the meaning of *posterior* apply to the posterior air sacs?

_____

_____

Circle the letter of the word or phrase that best completes the analogy.

3. Gas exchange is to lungs as storage is to

    a. air sacs.

    b. beak.

    c. trachea.

    d. bronchi.

CHAPTER 42 ACTIVE READING WORKSHEETS

BIRDS

Section 42-3: Classification

Read the passage below, which covers topics from your textbook. Answer the questions that follow.

> By looking closely at a bird's beak and feet, you can infer many things about where the bird lives and how it feeds. Hawks and eagles have powerful beaks and clawed talons that help them capture and tear apart their prey. Swifts have a tiny beak that opens wide like a catcher's mitt to snare insects in midair. Because swifts spend most of their lives in flight, their feet are small and adapted for infrequent perching. The feet of flightless birds, on the other hand, are modified for walking and running.

Read each question and write your answer in the space provided.

SKILL: Forming Analogies

1. Complete the following analogy: "Powerful beak is to hawk as tiny beak is to _____."

2. Complete the following analogy: "Swift is to infrequent perching as flightless bird is to

_____."

Read the question and write your answer in the space provided.

SKILL: Vocabulary Development

3. What is the meaning of the term *snare* in the passage?

_____

Circle the letter of the word or phrase that best completes the statement.

4. Small feet are to flight as clawed talons are to

   a. walking.
   b. running.
   c. capturing prey.
   d. Both (a) and (b)

MAMMALS

Section 43-1: Origin and Evolution of Mammals

Read the passage below, which covers topics from your textbook. Answer the questions that follow.

[1] The ancestors of mammals first appeared on Earth more than 300 million years ago. [2] At that time, a major evolutionary split occurred in the terrestrial vertebrates, producing two groups of animals. [3] Members of the first group gave rise to dinosaurs, birds, and all the living reptiles. [4] Members of the second group, known as **synapsids,** gave rise to mammals and their extinct relatives. [5] Mammals are the only surviving synapsids. [6] Early synapsids can be distinguished by the structure of their skull. [7] There is a single opening in the outer layer of the skull just behind the eye socket. [8] This same type of skull is found in all later synapsids, including mammals, although often in a highly modified form.

Read each question and write your answer in the space provided.

SKILL: Recognizing Text Structure

1. Text structure is the format an author uses to organize ideas. The author of this passage used a main idea and supporting details. What is the main idea of the passage?

   _____

   _____

   _____

2. What physical trait of synapsids is identified?

   _____

   _____

Circle the letter of the word that best completes the statement.

3. The only surviving synapsids are

   a. reptiles.
   b. mammals.
   c. birds.
   d. Both (a) and (b)

Name _____ Class _____ Date _____

MAMMALS

Section 43-2: Characteristics of Mammals

Read the passage below, which covers topics from your textbook. Answer the questions that follow.

Plants can be difficult to digest because they contain large amounts of cellulose, which is a polymer of glucose, and no vertebrates produce enzymes to break down cellulose. However, some mammals can digest cellulose with the aid of microorganisms. Cows, sheep, goats, giraffes, and many other hoofed mammals have a large stomach with four chambers. One chamber, known as the **rumen,** contains symbiotic bacteria and other microorganisms. After plant material is chewed and swallowed, it enters the rumen. Microorganisms then begin to break down the cellulose. The food is further digested in the rumen, then regurgitated, chewed again, and swallowed again. Food may be regurgitated and swallowed several times. Microorganisms that live in the rumen break down cellulose into small molecules that are eventually absorbed into the animal's bloodstream when the food reaches the small intestine.

In horses, rodents, rabbits, and elephants, microorganisms that live in the **cecum** complete digestion of food. The cecum is a large sac that branches from the small intestine and acts as a fermentation chamber. Food passes through the stomach and the small intestine before entering the cecum.

Fill in the blank to complete each sentence.

SKILL: Completing Sentences

1. Plants contain _____, which is a polymer of glucose.

2. Vertebrates lack the _____ needed to break down cellulose.

3. Some mammals can digest cellulose with the aid of _____.

4. Many hoofed mammals, such as cows and sheep, have a large _____ with four chambers.

5. The _____ contains symbiotic bacteria and other microorganisms.

6. Inside the rumen, microorganisms break down cellulose into small _____.

7. When the food reaches the animal's _____, the molecules are absorbed into the animal's bloodstream.

8. Microorganisms that live in the _____ of an elephant complete digestion of food.

9. The cecum is a large sac that branches from the _____.

10. The cecum acts as a _____ to aid digestion.

11. Before entering the cecum, food passes through the _____ and small intestine.

Read the question and write your answer in the space provided.

SKILL: Vocabulary Development

12. What is the meaning of the term *regurgitated* in the passage?

_____

_____

Circle the letter of the word that best completes the analogy.

13. Cecum is to rabbit as rumen is to

   a. horse.
   b. goat.
   c. elephant.
   d. Both (a) and (b)

CHAPTER 43 ACTIVE READING WORKSHEETS

MAMMALS

Section 43-3: Diversity of Mammals

Read the table below, which covers topics from your textbook.
Answer the questions that follow.

Minor Orders of Mammals		
Order	**Characteristic**	**Example**
Macroscelidea	ground-dwelling insectivores with long, flexible snouts; 15 species found only in Africa	elephant shrew
Pholidota	insectivores with protective scales composed of fused hair; resemble reptiles; found in Africa and southern Asia	pangolin
Tubulidentata	nearly hairless insectivores with pig-like bodies and long snouts; found in southern Africa	aardvark
Scandentia	squirrel-like omnivores that live on ground and in trees; feed on fruit and small animals; found in tropical Asia	tree shrew
Dermoptera	only two species exist; glide in air using a thin membrane stretched between their limbs; found only in parts of Asia	flying lemur
Hyracoidea	small rabbit-like herbivores; 7 species found only in Africa	hyrax

Read the question and write your answer in the space provided.

SKILL: Organizing Information

1. How does the movement of members of the order Dermoptera differ from members of the other orders?

_____

_____

Read the question and write your answer in the space provided.

SKILL: Vocabulary Development

2. What is the meaning of the term *insectivore* in the table?

_____

Circle the letter of the word that best completes the analogy.

3. Africa is to Hyracoidea as Asia is to

   a. Dermoptera.
   b. Tubulidentata.
   c. Macroscelidea.
   d. None of the above

CHAPTER 43 ACTIVE READING WORKSHEETS

MAMMALS

Section 43-4: Primates and Human Origins

**Read the passage below, which covers topics from your textbook.
Answer the questions that follow.**

Prosimians include lemurs, lorises, and tarsiers. **Anthropoid primates** include New World monkeys, Old World monkeys, and apes, including humans. Anthropoid adaptations include rotating shoulder and elbow joints and an **opposable thumb,** which can touch the other fingers. All anthropoids have a similar dental formula, or number and arrangement of teeth. Each half of the upper and lower mouth includes two incisors, one canine, two premolars, and three molars. Compared to other primates, anthropoids have a more complex brain structure and a larger brain relative to body size.

Read the questions and write your answer in the space provided.

SKILL: Recognizing Text Structure

1. Text structure is the format an author uses to organize ideas. The author of this passage used a main idea and supporting details. What is the main idea of the passage?

   _____

2. What are three supporting ideas of the main idea?

   _____

   _____

   _____

Circle the letter of the word or phrase that best answers the question.

3. Which of the following is NOT an anthropoid primate?

   a. human
   b. ape
   c. lemur
   d. new world monkey

CHAPTER 44 ACTIVE READING WORKSHEETS

ANIMAL BEHAVIOR

Section 44-1: Development of Behavior

Read the passage below, which covers topics from your textbook. Answer the questions that follow.

When studying behavior, ethologists often ask how much of an animal's behavior is determined by genetics and how much of the behavior varies based on the animal's environment. Studies of bees provide information about genes and behavior. Adult "hygienic" bees can detect which young in the hive have bacterial infections and pull these young from their cells and throw them out of the hive. "Nonhygienic" adults ignore diseased young. Mating hygienic queens to nonhygienic males showed that certain genes control young-removal behavior. The triggers for the behavior, however, are environmental. In this case, diseased young present in the hive trigger the removal behavior.

Fill in the blanks to complete each sentence.

SKILL: Completing Sentences

1. Studies show that _____ control young-removal behavior.

2. The trigger for young-removal behavior is _____.

3. Hygienic adult bees throw _____

    _____ out of the hive.

4. Nonhygienic adult bees _____ diseased young.

Read the question and write your answer in the space provided.

SKILL: Vocabulary Development

5. What is the meaning of the term *hygienic* in the passage?

    _____

Name _____ Class _____ Date _____

ANIMAL BEHAVIOR

Section 44-2: Types of Animal Behavior

Read the passage below, which covers topics from your textbook. Answer the questions that follow.

Most scientists have regarded language as a uniquely human behavior. In order for communication to be considered language, there are certain criteria that must be met. Among these are phonemes (sounds that can be combined to form words), productivity (many combinations of phonemes to produce different meanings), and grammar (rules for combining words that affect the meaning). Most animal communication lacks at least one of the characteristics of true language. Although animals do not use language systems for communication in the wild, it is possible that they can learn to use them. Research on language is being done with gorillas, chimpanzees, bonobos, parrots, dogs, and dolphins.

Read each question and write your answer in the space provided.

SKILL: Recognizing Text Structure

1. Text structure is the form an author uses to organize ideas. The author of this passage used a main idea and supporting details. What is the main idea of the passage?

_____

2. What are the supporting details of the passage?

_____

Circle the letter of the word or phrase that best completes the analogy.

3. Phoneme is to combining sounds as grammar is to

   a. productivity.
   b. combining words.
   c. combining phonemes.
   d. true language.

Name _____ Class _____ Date _____

SKELETAL, MUSCULAR, AND INTEGUMENTARY SYSTEMS

Section 45-1: The Human Body Plan

Read the table below, which covers topics from your textbook. Answer the questions that follow.

Summary of Organ Systems		
System	**Major structures**	**Functions**
Skeletal	bone	provides structure; supports and protects internal organs
Muscular	muscles (skeletal, cardiac, and smooth)	provides structure; supports and moves trunk and limbs; moves substance through body
Integumentary	skin, hair, nails	protects against pathogens; helps regulate body temperature
Cardiovascular	heart, blood vessels, blood	transports nutrients and wastes to and from all body tissues
Respiratory	air passages, lungs	carries air into and out of lungs
Immune	lymph nodes and vessels, white blood cells	provides protection against infection and disease
Digestive	mouth, esophagus, stomach, liver, pancreas, small and large intestine	stores and digests food; absorbs nutrients; eliminates waste
Excretory	kidneys, ureters, bladder, urethra, skin, lungs	eliminates waste; maintains water and chemical balance
Nervous	brain, spinal cord, nerves, sense organs, receptors	controls and coordinates body movements and senses; controls consciousness and creativity; helps monitor and maintain other body systems
Endocrine	glands (such as adrenal, thyroid, and pancreas), hypothalamus	maintains homeostasis; regulated metabolism, water and mineral balance, growth, development, and reproduction
Reproductive	ovaries, uterus, mammary glands (in females), testes (in males)	produces eggs and milk in females, sperm in males; produces offspring

Read the question and write your answer in the space provided.

SKILL: Vocabulary Development

1. The term *immune* is derived from a Latin word that means "exempt from service." How is the term *immune system* related to the meaning of its term of origin?

_____

continued on the next page . . .

Name _____ Class _____ Date _____

Read each question and write your answer in the space provided.

SKILL: Forming Analogies

An analogy identifies a similar relationship between different pairs of items. In an analogy, one must analyze the relationship between two words and then identify another pair of words that have the same relationship. An example is "Glove is to hand as sock is to the foot," where the relationship is article of clothing to where it is worn.

2. What relationship was used to form the analogy "Blood vessels are to circulatory as hair is to integumentary"?

_____

3. Complete the following analogy: "Skeletal is to support as immune is to

_____."

4. What relationship was used to form the analogy in question 3?

_____

Circle the letter of the word or phrase that best completes the analogy.

5. Excretory is to ureters as immune is to

   a. esophagus.
   b. hypothalamus.
   c. lymph nodes.
   d. receptors.

Write the answer to each question on the line provided.

SKILL: Organizing Information

6. What two organ systems do the lungs belong to?

_____

7. What two organ systems do white blood cells belong to?

_____

8. Which organ systems enable reproduction?

_____

SKELETAL, MUSCULAR, AND INTEGUMENTARY SYSTEMS

Section 45-2: Skeletal System

Read the passage below, which covers topics from your textbook. Answer the questions that follow.

The place where two bones meet is known as a **joint.** Three major kinds of joints are found in the human body. **Fixed joints** prevent movement. They are found in the skull, where they securely connect the bony plates and permit no movement of these bones. A small amount of connective tissue in a fixed joint helps absorb impact to prevent the bones from breaking.

Semimovable joints permit limited movement. For example, semimovable joints hold the bones of the vertebral column in place and allow the body to bend and twist. The vertebrae of the spine are separated by discs of cartilaginous tissue. These tough, springy disks compress and absorb shocks that could damage the fragile spinal cord.

Most of the joints of the body are **movable joints.** Movable joints include hinge, ball-and-socket, pivot, saddle, and gliding joints. An example of a *hinge joint* is found in the elbow, which allows you to move your forearm upward and downward. An example of a *ball-and-socket joint* is the shoulder joint. The joint formed by the two top vertebrae of your spine is an example of a *pivot joint.* The *saddle joint,* found at the base of each thumb, allows you to rotate your thumbs and helps you grasp objects with your hand. Finally, *gliding joints* allow bones to slide over one another. Examples are the joints between the small bones of your foot, which allow your foot to flex when you walk.

Read the question and write your answer in the space provided.

SKILL: Vocabulary Development

1. The prefix *semi-* means "half or partially." How does knowledge of this word part aid in describing *semimovable joints*?

_____

continued on the next page . . .

Read each description. On the line, identify the type of joint described.

SKILL: Organizing Information

_____ 2. allows you to rotate your thumbs

_____ 3. is found in the elbow

_____ 4. allows bones to slide over one another

_____ 5. prevents movement

_____ 6. is found in the shoulder

Circle the letter of the phrase that best completes the statement.

7. The function of the small amount of connective tissue in a fixed joint is to

    a. facilitate movement.
    b. absorb impact.
    c. connect muscles.
    d. Both (a) and (b)

SKELETAL, MUSCULAR, AND INTEGUMENTARY SYSTEMS

Section 45-3 Muscular System

Read the passage below, which covers topics from your textbook. Answer the questions that follow.

Most skeletal muscles are arranged in opposing pairs. One muscle in a pair moves a limb in one direction; the other muscle moves it in the opposite direction. Muscles move bones by pulling them, not pushing them. For example, when the biceps muscle contracts, the arm bends at the elbow. The biceps muscle is known as a **flexor,** a muscle that bends a joint. Contraction of the triceps muscle in the upper arm straightens the limb. The triceps muscle is an example of an **extensor,** a muscle that straightens a joint. To bring about a smooth movement, one muscle in a pair must relax while the opposing muscle contracts.

Read each question and write your answer in the space provided.

SKILL: Recognizing Cause-and-Effect Relationships

1. What causes bones to move?

_____

2. What is the effect of contraction of the biceps muscle?

_____

3. What is the effect of contraction of the triceps muscle?

_____

Circle the letter of the word that completes the analogy.

4. Extensor is to straighten as flexor is to

    a. bend.
    b. push.
    c. expand.
    d. Both (a) and (b)

Name _____ Class _____ Date _____

SKELETAL, MUSCULAR, AND INTEGUMENTARY SYSTEMS

Section 45-4: Integumentary System

Read the passage below, which covers topics from your textbook. Answer the questions that follow.

The skin contains **exocrine glands,** glands that release secretions through ducts. The main exocrine glands of the skin are the sweat glands and the oil glands. The skin functions as an excretory organ by releasing excess water, salts, and urea through the **sweat glands.** By releasing excess water, the skin also helps regulate body temperature.

Oil glands, found in large numbers on the face and scalp, secrete a fatty substance known as **sebum.** Oil glands are usually connected by tiny ducts to hair follicles. Sebum coats the surface of the skin and the shafts of hairs, preventing excess water loss and lubricating and softening the skin and hair. If the ducts of oil glands become clogged with excessive amounts of sebum, dead cells, and bacteria, the skin disorder *acne* can result.

Read each question and write your answer in the space provided.

SKILL: Recognizing Text Structure

1. What type of text structure did the author use in the above passage?

   _____

2. What are the similarities and differences between sweat glands and oil glands?

   _____

   _____

Circle the letter of the word that best completes the sentence.

3. Large numbers of oil glands are located on the

   a. scalp.
   b. face.
   c. hands.
   d. Both (a) and (b)

CHAPTER 46 ACTIVE READING WORKSHEETS

CIRCULATORY AND RESPIRATORY SYSTEMS

Section 46-1: The Circulatory System

**Read the passage below, which covers topics from your textbook.
Answer the questions that follow.**

Systemic circulation is the movement of blood between the heart and all parts of the body except the lungs. Oxygenated blood is pumped out of the left ventricle and into the aorta. From the aorta, blood flows into other subsystems of systemic circulation.

Coronary circulation is one subsystem of systemic circulation that supplies blood to the heart itself. If the blood supply to the heart is reduced or cut off, muscle cells will die. This can happen when an artery is blocked by a blood clot or by **atherosclerosis,** a disease characterized by the buildup of fatty materials on the interior wall of the coronary artery. If either type of blockage reduces the flow of blood to the heart muscle cells, a heart attack will result.

Hepatic portal circulation is a subsystem of systemic circulation. Nutrients are picked up by capillaries in the small intestine and are transported by the blood to the liver. Excess nutrients are stored in the liver for future needs. The liver receives oxygenated blood from a large artery that branches from the aorta.

Renal circulation, another subsystem of systemic circulation, supplies blood to the kidneys. Nearly one-fourth of the blood that is pumped into the aorta by the left ventricle flows to the kidneys. The kidneys filter waste from the blood.

Read each question and write your answer in the space provided.

SKILL: Recognizing Similarities and Differences

1. What are the three subsystems of systemic circulation?

_____

_____

continued on the next page . . .

2. What are the differences between these three subsystems?

_____

_____

_____

_____

Read the question and write your answer in the space provided.

SKILL: Vocabulary Development

3. The term *renal* comes from a Latin word meaning "kidneys." How does knowledge of the origin of *renal* aid in defining *renal circulation*?

_____

Circle the letter of the word or phrase that best completes the sentence.

4. Atherosclerosis is a disease characterized by the buildup of fatty materials on the interior walls of the

    a. kidneys.
    b. liver.
    c. coronary artery.
    d. aorta.

CIRCULATORY AND RESPIRATORY SYSTEMS

Section 46-2: Blood

Read the passage below, which covers topics from your textbook. Answer the questions that follow.

When a blood vessel tears or rips, platelets congregate at the damaged site, sticking together and forming a plug. The vessel constricts, slowing blood flow to the area. Then special clotting factors are released from the platelets and the damaged tissue. These factors begin a series of chemical reactions that occur at the site of the bleeding. The last step in this series brings about the production of a protein called **fibrin.** Fibrin molecules consist of long, sticky chains. These chains form a net that traps red blood cells, and the mass of fibrin and red blood cells hardens into a clot, or scab.

Write your answers in the spaces provided.

SKILL: Sequencing Information

1. Order the statements to show the steps of the blood-clotting process. Write "1" on the line in front of the statement that describes what happens first. Write "2" on the line in front of the statement that describes what happens next, and so on.

_____ **a.** Long, sticky chains of fibrin are produced.

_____ **b.** Platelets congregate at the site of injury.

_____ **c.** Fibrin chains form a net to trap red blood cells.

_____ **d.** A blood vessel is torn.

_____ **e.** The blood vessel constricts.

_____ **f.** Platelets release special clotting factors.

Circle the letter of the word or phrase that best completes the analogy.

2. Platelets are to plug as fibrin is to

   a. blood.   **c.** net.

   b. red blood cells.   **d.** chemical reaction.

Name _____ Class _____ Date _____

CIRCULATORY AND RESPIRATORY SYSTEMS

Section 46-3: The Respiratory System

Read the passage below, which covers topics from your textbook. Answer the questions that follow.

External respiration begins at the mouth and at the nose. Air filters through the small hairs of the nose and passes into the nasal cavity, located above the roof of the mouth. In the nasal cavity, mucous membranes warm and moisten the air, which helps prevent damage to the delicate tissues that form the respiratory system. The moistened, filtered air then moves into the **pharynx,** a tube at the back of the nasal cavities and the mouth. The pharynx contains passageways for both food and air. When food is swallowed, a flap of cartilage called the **epiglottis** presses down and covers the opening to the air passage. When air is being taken in, the epiglottis is in an upright position, allowing air to pass into a cartilaginous tube called the **trachea.** The trachea is about 10 to 12 cm long and has walls lined with ciliated cells that trap inhaled particles. The cilia sweep the particles and mucus away from the lungs toward the throat.

At the upper end of the trachea is the **larynx.** Sounds are produced when air is forced past two ligaments—the vocal cords—that stretch across the larynx. Past the larynx the trachea branches into two **bronchi,** each of which leads to a lung. The walls of the bronchi consist of smooth muscle and cartilage and are lined with cilia and mucus. Within the lungs, the bronchi branch into smaller and smaller tubes. The smallest of these tubes are known as **bronchioles,** which are also lined with cilia and mucus. Eventually the bronchioles end in clusters of tiny air sacs called **alveoli.** All exchange of gases in the lungs occurs in the alveoli.

Read the question and write your answer in the space provided.

SKILL: Vocabulary Development

1. What is the meaning of the term *cartilaginous* in the passage?

Read each description. Write on the line the part of the respiratory system being described.

SKILL: Organizing Information

_____ **2.** Sounds are produced here.

_____ **3.** All exchange of gases in the lungs occurs here.

_____ **4.** Moistened, filtered air goes here after leaving the nasal cavities.

_____ **5.** This cartilage flap can cover the opening to the air passage.

_____ **6.** These two large tubes lead to the lungs.

Observe the figure below. Write the correct label on the line provided.

SKILL: Interpreting Graphics

7. The diagram below shows the parts of the respiratory system. Write the following labels on the diagram: "Alveoli," "Bronchus," "Bronchiole," "Epiglottis," "Larynx," "Lung," "Pharynx," and "Trachea." Write your answers on the lines.

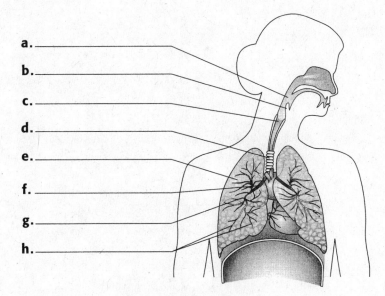

a. _____

b. _____

c. _____

d. _____

e. _____

f. _____

g. _____

h. _____

Circle the letter of the word that best completes the statement.

8. Cilia in trachea trap inhaled particles and sweep them toward the

   a. lungs.
   b. capillaries.
   c. alveoli.
   d. throat.

CHAPTER 47 ACTIVE READING WORKSHEETS

THE BODY'S DEFENSE SYSTEMS

Section 47-1: Nonspecific Defenses

Read the passage below, which covers topics from your textbook. Answer the questions that follow.

Any pathogen that penetrates the skin or a mucous membrane will stimulate a nonspecific defense mechanism called the **inflammatory response,** a series of events that suppress infection and speed recovery. When cells are damaged, some of the damaged cells release histamine. **Histamine** increases blood flow to the injured area and increases the permeability of the surrounding capillaries. As a result, fluids and white blood cells pass through capillary walls to the injured area.

If blood cells have been damaged by the injury, platelets and clotting proteins initiate the blood-clotting process, sealing off the surrounding tissues and preventing pathogens from invading the rest of the body. The release of histamine attracts white blood cells to the site of the injury. Among the white blood cells that respond are phagocytes, which ingest and destroy pathogens.

Read each question and write your answer in the space provided.

SKILL: Recognizing Cause-and-Effect Relationships

1. What causes an inflammatory response?

_____

2. What causes initiation of the blood-clotting process?

_____

Circle the letter of the phrase that best completes the statement.

3. Histamines cause

   a. increases in permeability of capillaries.
   b. increased blood flow to the injured area.

   c. destruction of a pathogen.
   d. Both (a) and (b)

CHAPTER 47 ACTIVE READING WORKSHEETS

THE BODY'S DEFENSE SYSTEMS

Section 47-2: Specific Defenses: The Immune System

Read the passage below, which covers topics from your textbook.
Answer the questions that follow.

Immunity is the ability to resist or recover from an infectious
disease. One way to gain immunity is to be infected by a pathogen,
undergo a primary immune response, and survive the disease the
pathogen causes. Another, safer way is through vaccination. Vaccines contain dead or weakened pathogens or material from a
pathogen. However, the antigens are still present, so the body produces a primary immune response to the antigens in the vaccine.
The memory cells that remain after the primary immune response
can provide a quick secondary immune response if the antigen
ever enters the body again. Some of the diseases that have been
controlled through the use of vaccines are polio, measles, mumps,
tetanus, and diphtheria.

Read each question and write your answer in the space provided.

SKILL: Identifying Main Ideas

1. What is the main idea of this passage?

   _____

   _____

2. What are some diseases that have been controlled through the use of vaccines?

   _____

Circle the letter of the word or phrase that best completes the analogy.

3. Pathogen is to disease as vaccine is to

   a. dead pathogen.
   b. immunity.
   c. antigen.
   d. Both (a) and (b)

CHAPTER 47 ACTIVE READING WORKSHEETS

THE BODY'S DEFENSE SYSTEMS

Section 47-3: HIV and AIDS

Read the passage below, which covers topics from your textbook.
Answer the questions that follow.

Scientists trying to create vaccines for HIV must contend with its rapid rate of evolution. The genes that code for the virus's surface proteins mutate frequently. As a result, new variants of the virus with slightly different surface proteins are constantly appearing. To produce effective immunity, a vaccine against HIV must stimulate the immune system to respond to many variants of the virus. Although several vaccines against HIV are under development or being tested, none has yet proven effective.

Due to HIV's rapid evolution, it can quickly become resistant to drugs. Scientists now treat patients with a combination of three drugs. Because mutations are random, mutations that create resistance to all three drugs are not likely to occur.

Fill in the blank to complete each sentence.

SKILL: Completing Sentences

1. An effective _____ against the HIV virus must stimulate the immune system to respond to many variants of the virus.

2. The HIV virus quickly becomes _____ to drugs used against it.

3. Scientists have begun treating HIV patients with _____.

Circle the letter of the phrase that best completes the statement.

4. Several vaccines against HIV are

   a. being tested.
   b. under development.
   c. producing effective immunity against the virus.
   d. Both (a) and (b)

Name _____ Class _____ Date _____

DIGESTIVE AND EXCRETORY SYSTEMS

Section 48-1: Nutrients

Read the table below, which covers topics from your textbook.
Answer the questions that follow.

Food Sources of Minerals		
Minerals	**Source**	**Essential for**
Calcium	milk, whole-grain cereals, vegetables, meats	deposition in bones and teeth; functioning of heart, muscles, and nerves
Iodine	seafoods, water, iodized salt	thyroid hormone production
Iron	leafy vegetables, liver, meats, raisins, prunes	formation of hemoglobin in red blood cells
Magnesium	vegetables	muscle and nerve action
Phosphorus	milk, whole-grain cereals, vegetables, meats	deposition in bones and teeth; formation of ATP and nucleic acids
Potassium	vegetables, citrus fruits, bananas, apricots	maintaining acid-base balance; growth; nerve action
Sodium	table salt, vegetables	blood and other body tissues; muscle and nerve action

Read each question and write your answer in the space provided.

SKILL: Forming Analogies

1. Complete the following analogy: "Liver is to iron as apricot is to _____."

2. Complete the following analogy: "Phosphorus is to ATP and nucleic acids as iron is to

_____."

3. Complete the following analogy: "Water is to iodine as milk is to _____."

Circle the letter of the word or phrase that best completes the statement.

4. Vegetables are a primary source of all the minerals listed in the table EXCEPT

   a. iodine.
   b. magnesium.
   c. sodium.
   d. iron.

Name _____ Class _____ Date _____

DIGESTIVE AND EXCRETORY SYSTEMS

Section 48-2: Digestive System

Read the passage below, which covers topics from your textbook.
Answer the questions that follow.

The **liver** is a large organ located to the right of the stomach. The liver performs numerous functions in the body, including storing glucose as glycogen, making proteins, and breaking down toxic substances, such as alcohol. The liver also secretes bile, which is vital in the digestion of fats. Bile breaks fat globules into small droplets, forming a milky fluid in which fats are suspended. This process exposes a greater surface area of fats to the action of digestive enzymes and prevents small fat droplets from rejoining into large globules.

The bile secreted by the liver passes through a Y-shaped duct. The bile travels down one branch of the Y and then up the other branch to the **gallbladder,** a saclike organ that stores and concentrates the bile. When chyme is present in the small intestine, the gallbladder releases bile through the common bile duct into the small intestine.

Write the answer to each question in the space provided.

SKILL: Identifying Main Ideas

1. What are three functions of the liver?

_____

_____

2. If bile is not a digestive enzyme, how can it aid in the digestion of fats?

_____

_____

3. What is the function of the gallbladder?

_____

_____

Write your answers in the spaces provided.

SKILL: Interpreting Graphics

4. The diagram below illustrates parts of the digestive system. Complete the diagram by adding the following labels: "Common bile duct," "Main pancreatic duct," "Gallbladder," "Liver," "Pancreas," "Small intestine," and "Stomach."

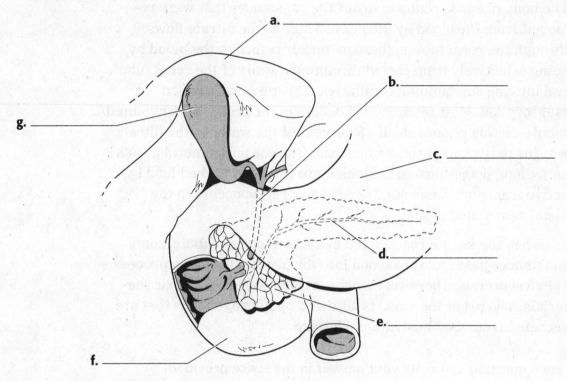

a. _____

b. _____

c. _____

d. _____

e. _____

f. _____

g. _____

Read the question and write your answer in the space provided.

SKILL: Vocabulary Development

5. Compare the meaning of the term *suspended* in the passage with its meaning in the sentence "The intoxicated driver will have his license suspended."

_____

_____

_____

Circle the letter of the phrase that best completes the statement.

6. The gallbladder releases bile into the small intestine when

    a. fats are present in the stomach.   **c.** chyme is present in the small intestine.

    b. glycogen is present in the liver.   **d.** fats are present in the small intestine.

CHAPTER 48 ACTIVE READING WORKSHEETS

DIGESTIVE AND EXCRETORY SYSTEMS

Section 48-3: Urinary System

Read the passage below, which covers topics from your textbook. Answer the questions that follow.

The body needs to retain many of the substances that were removed from the blood by filtration. Thus, as the filtrate flows through the renal tubule, these materials return to the blood by being selectively transported through the walls of the renal tubule and into the surrounding capillaries. This process is called **reabsorption.** Most reabsorption occurs in the proximal convoluted tubule. In this region, about 75 percent of the water in the filtrate returns to the capillaries by osmosis. Glucose and minerals, such as sodium, potassium, and calcium, are returned to the blood by active transport. Some additional reabsorption occurs in the distal convoluted tubule.

When the filtrate reaches the distal convoluted tubule, some substances pass from the blood into the filtrate through a process called **secretion.** These substances include wastes and toxic materials. The pH of the blood is adjusted by hydrogen ions that are secreted from the blood into the filtrate.

Read each question and write your answer in the space provided.

SKILL: Recognizing Similarities and Differences

1. How do reabsorption and secretion affect homeostasis?

_____

2. How does the movement of substances differ in reabsorption and secretion?

_____

_____

Circle the letter of the word that best completes the sentence.

3. Through reabsorption, the body retains all of the following substances EXCEPT

   a. potassium.   **c.** glucose.
   b. helium.   **d.** sodium.

CHAPTER 49 ACTIVE READING WORKSHEETS

NERVOUS SYSTEM AND SENSE ORGANS

Section 49-1: Neurons and Nerve Impulses

**Read the passage below, which covers topics from your textbook.
Answer the questions that follow.**

When a dendrite or the cell body of a neuron is stimulated, a sudden change occurs in the permeability of its cell membrane. At the point where it is stimulated, the cell membrane becomes permeable to Na^+ ions. The rush of Na^+ ions into the cell opens voltage-gated channels in the membrane that allow even more Na^+ ions to diffuse rapidly from the outside of the membrane to the inside of the neuron. As a result of the inward diffusion of Na^+ ions, the interior of the neuron's cell body becomes more positively charged than the outer surface. The interior, once negatively charged, is now positively charged. The exterior, once positively charged, is now negatively charged with respect to the interior. This reversal of polarity across the membrane begins an action potential. The action potential starts at the point where the cell body of the neuron joins the axon.

Voltage-gated channels exist along the entire length of the axon. As the first small segment of the axon becomes positively charged, the change in voltage opens channels in the next segment of axon membrane. As before, Na^+ ions enter, driving the voltage in a positive direction and opening channels in the next segment of the axon.

Shortly after they open, the voltage-gated channels for the Na^+ ions close. Then voltage-gated channels for K^+ ions open. The result is an abrupt outward flow of K^+ ions. The outer surface again becomes positively charged, and the inner surface regains its negative charge. This signals the end of the action potential.

Read the question and write your answer in the space provided.

SKILL: Vocabulary Development

1. The term *permeable* comes from a Latin word that means "to penetrate." How is the term *permeable* related to its word of origin?

_____

continued on the next page . . .

Write your answers in the spaces provided.

SKILL: Sequencing Information

2. Order the statements to show the changes that occur during an action potential. Write "1" on the line in front of the statement that describes what happens first. Write "2" on the line in front of the statement that describes what happens next, and so on.

_____ **a.** Na+ ions diffuse into the neuron.

_____ **b.** The action potential ends.

_____ **c.** The cell membrane becomes permeable to Na^+ ions.

_____ **d.** The gated channels for Na^+ ions close.

_____ **e.** The interior of the neuron's cell body becomes more positively charged than the outer surface.

_____ **f.** Voltage-gated channels for K^+ ions open.

_____ **g.** Voltage-gated channels open.

_____ **h.** The inner surface of the neuron's cell body regains its negative charge.

_____ **i.** A positive charge passes down the membrane of the axon.

_____ **j.** A dendrite or cell body of a neuron is stimulated.

_____ **k.** Additional Na^+ channels in the axon membrane open until the whole neuron is positively charged.

_____ **l.** A stream of K^+ ions flows outward.

Circle the letter of the phrase that best completes the statement.

3. An action potential begins at a point where the cell body of a neuron

   a. joins the axon.
   b. is selectively permeable.
   c. has more Na^+ ions than K^+ ions.
   d. Both (a) and (b)

CHAPTER 49 ACTIVE READING WORKSHEETS

NERVOUS SYSTEM AND SENSE ORGANS

Section 49-2: Structure of the Nervous System

Read the passage below, which covers topics from your textbook. Answer the questions that follow.

[1] The motor division of the peripheral nervous system is composed of two independent systems—the somatic nervous system and the autonomic nervous system. [2] The **somatic nervous system** consists of motor neurons that control the movement of skeletal muscles. [3] The somatic system is said to be voluntary—that is, skeletal muscles can be moved at will. [4] The somatic system can also operate without conscious control, as it does when you maintain your balance.

[5] The **autonomic nervous system** consists of nerves that control the body's internal conditions by regulating smooth muscles, both in blood vessels and in organs. [6] The autonomic nervous system controls respiration, heartbeat, digestion, and other functions of homeostasis.

Read each question and write your answer in the space provided.

SKILL: Recognizing Text Structure

1. The author of this passage used a main idea and supporting details. What is the main idea of the passage?

   _____

   _____

2. What supporting detail does Sentence 6 provide the reader?

   _____

   _____

Circle the letter of the word or phrase that best completes the analogy.

3. The somatic nervous system is to skeletal muscles as the autonomic nervous system is to

   a. bones.
   b. smooth muscles.
   c. nerves.
   d. skin.

NERVOUS SYSTEM AND SENSE ORGANS

Section 49-3: Sensory Systems

**Read the passage below, which covers topics from your textbook.
Answer the questions that follow.**

A sensory receptor is a neuron that is specialized to detect a stimulus. There are many kinds of sensory receptors, and they can be categorized on the basis of the types of stimuli to which they respond.

- *Mechanoreceptors* respond to movement, pressure, and tension.

- *Photoreceptors* respond to variations in light.

- *Chemoreceptors* respond to chemicals.

- *Thermoreceptors* respond to changes in temperature.

- *Pain receptors* respond to tissue damage.

Sensory receptors are found in high concentrations in the **sense organs**—the eyes, ears, nose, mouth, and skin—and in fewer numbers throughout the rest of the body.

Read each question and write your answer in the space provided.

SKILL: Forming Analogies

1. Complete the following analogy: "Mechanoreceptor is to pressure as pain receptor is to

_____."

2. Complete the following analogy: "Neuron is to sensory receptor as ears are to _____."

Circle the letter of the word or phrase that best completes the statement.

3. Photoreceptors and thermoreceptors are alike in that both respond to

   a. the same stimuli.
   b. variations in a stimulus.
   c. tension.
   d. tissue damage.

NERVOUS SYSTEM AND SENSE ORGANS

Section 49-4: Drugs and the Nervous System

Read the passage below, which covers topics from your textbook. Answer the questions that follow.

Alcohol is a **depressant,** a drug that decreases the activity of the central nervous system. Alcohol increases circulation to the skin, decreases blood flow to internal organs, and lowers body temperature. Alcohol causes the kidneys to excrete more water, which can cause dehydration. As drinking continues, judgment and coordination become impaired, speech slurs, and reaction time lengthens. Respiration rate slows after an initial increase. High doses of alcohol can cause death by respiratory failure. The severity of these effects depends largely on **blood alcohol concentration** (BAC), a measurement of the amount of alcohol in the blood.

Read each question and write your answer in the space provided.

SKILL: Recognizing Text Structure

1. The passage includes a main idea and supporting details. What is the main idea of the passage?

   _____

   _____

2. What supporting details are provided in the passage?

   _____

   _____

   _____

Circle the letter of the word or phrase that best completes the statement.

3. With increasing BAC levels, the effect of alcohol on the central nervous system

   a. decreases.
   b. increases.
   c. remains about the same.
   d. fluctuates between increasing and decreasing.

_____

_____

_____

_____

_____

_____

CHAPTER 50 ACTIVE READING WORKSHEETS

ENDOCRINE SYSTEM

Section 50-1: Hormones

Read the passage below, which covers topics from your textbook. Answer the questions that follow.

Hormones are made and secreted by endocrine glands. **Endocrine glands** are ductless organs that secrete hormones either into the bloodstream or the fluid around cells. Specialized cells in the brain, stomach, small intestine, liver, heart, and other organs also make and release hormones.

Exocrine glands secrete substances through ducts (tubelike structures). These substances can include water, enzymes, and mucus. The ducts transport the substances to specific locations inside and outside the body. Sweat glands, mucous glands, and salivary glands are exocrine glands.

Read the question and write your answer in the space provided.

SKILL: Recognizing Text Structure

1. The author of this passage used a similarities and differences text structure. What items are compared in the passage?

_____

Read the question and write your answer in the space provided.

SKILL: Vocabulary Development

2. What is the meaning of *ductless* in the passage?

_____

_____

Circle the letter of the phrase that best completes the statement.

3. All of the following are classified as exocrine glands EXCEPT

    a. salivary glands.
    b. mucous glands.
    c. pituitary glands.
    d. sweat glands.

CHAPTER 50 ACTIVE READING WORKSHEETS

ENDOCRINE SYSTEM

Section 50-2: Endocrine Glands

Read the table below, which covers topics from your textbook.
Answer the questions that follow.

Summary of Major Endocrine Glands and Their Functions		
Glands	**Hormone**	**Function**
Adrenal cortex		
	aldosterone	maintains salt-and-water balance
	cortisol	regulates carbohydrate and protein metabolism
Adrenal medulla	epinephrine	initiates body's response to stress and the
	norepinephrine	"fight or flight" response to danger
Ovaries	estrogen	regulates female secondary sex characteristics
	progesterone	maintains growth of uterine lining
Pancreas (islets of Langerhans)	glucagon	stimulates release of glucose
	insulin	stimulates absorption of glucose
Parathyroid glands	parathyroid hormone	increases blood calcium concentration
Pineal gland	melatonin	regulates sleep patterns
Testes	androgens (testosterone)	regulates male secondary sex characteristics; stimulates sperm production
Thymus gland	thymosin	stimulates T-cell formation
Thyroid gland	thyroxine, triiodothyronine	increase cellular metabolic rates

Use the table to answer the following questions. Write your answers on the lines
provided.

SKILL: Interpreting Graphics

1. Why do some rows have two entries in the column labeled "Hormone"?

_____

_____

2. What are the similarities and differences between the functions of estrogen and androgens?

_____

_____

_____

3. What are the similarities and differences between glucagon and insulin?

_____

_____

_____

Read each description. On the line, write the name of the gland described.

_____ **4.** It produces epinephrine and norepinephrine.

_____ **5.** The hormone it releases increases cellular metabolic rates.

_____ **6.** The hormone it releases regulates sleep patterns.

_____ **7.** It produces aldosterone and cortisol.

_____ **8.** The hormone it releases increases blood calcium concentration.

_____ **9.** One hormone it releases maintains growth of the uterine lining.

_____ **10.** It produces glucagon and insulin.

_____ **11.** The hormone it releases stimulates T-cell formation.

Read the question and write your answer in the space provided.

SKILL: **Vocabulary Development**

12. The term *stimulates* comes from a Latin word that means "to goad on." How is the term *stimulates* related to its term of origin?

_____

_____

Circle the letter of the word that best completes the analogy.

13. Sleep patterns are to melatonin as carbohydrate and protein metabolism is to

    a. cortisol.
    b. epinephrine.
    c. triiodothyronine.
    d. aldosterone.

REPRODUCTIVE SYSTEM

Section 51-1: Male Reproductive System

Read the passage below, which covers topics from your textbook. Answer the questions that follow.

A mature sperm consists of three regions—a head, a midpiece, and a tail. The tip of the head region contains enzymes. During fertilization, these enzymes help the sperm penetrate the protective layers that surround an egg cell. Also located in the head region are the 23 chromosomes that will be delivered to the egg. The midpiece is packed with mitochondria. These mitochondria supply the energy that is required for sperm to reach an egg. The tail consists of a single, powerful flagellum that propels the sperm.

Read each question and write your answer in the space provided.

SKILL: Identifying Main Ideas

1. What is the main idea of this passage?

_____

_____

2. How does the head of a sperm aid fertilization?

_____

_____

3. How does the midpiece aid fertilization?

_____

_____

4. What is the function of a sperm's tail?

_____

_____

continued on the next page . . .

Observe the figure below and write the correct labels on the lines provided.

5. The diagram below shows the structure of a human sperm. Complete the diagram by inserting the following labels: "Enzymes," "Head," "Midpiece," "Mitochondria," "Nucleus," and "Tail."

SKILL: Interpreting Graphics

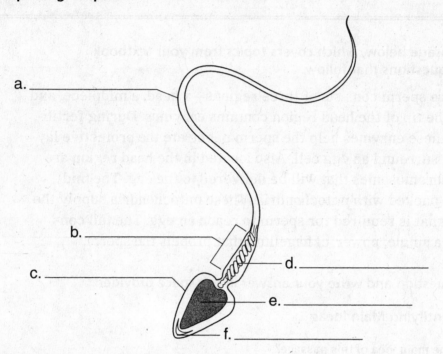

a. _____

b. _____

c. _____

d. _____

e. _____

f. _____

Read the question and write your answer in the space provided.

SKILL: Vocabulary Development

6. What is the meaning of the term *mature* in the passage?

_____

Circle the letter of the word that best answers the question.

7. Which part of a sperm contains the 23 chromosomes that are delivered to an egg through fertilization?

    a. mitochondria
    b. tail
    c. midpiece
    d. head

CHAPTER 51 ACTIVE READING WORKSHEETS

REPRODUCTIVE SYSTEM

Section 51-2: Female Reproductive System

**Read the passage below, which covers topics from your textbook.
Answer the questions that follow.**

The female reproductive system contains two almond-shaped ovaries that are located in the lower abdomen. Eggs mature near the surface of the ovaries, which are about 3.5 cm (1.4 in.) long and 2 cm (0.8 in.) in diameter. A mature egg is released into the abdominal cavity, where it is swept by cilia into the opening of a nearby **fallopian tube,** or uterine tube. The fallopian tube leads to the uterus. The **uterus** is a hollow, muscular organ about the size of a fist. If an egg is fertilized, it will develop in the uterus.

The lower entrance to the uterus is called the **cervix.** A sphincter muscle in the cervix controls the opening to the uterus. Leading from the cervix to the outside of the body is a muscular tube called the **vagina.** The vagina receives sperm from the penis; it is also the channel through which a baby passes during childbirth. The external structures of the female reproductive system are collectively called the **vulva.** The vulva includes the **labia,** folds of skin and mucous membranes that cover and protect the opening to the female reproductive system.

Read each description. On the line provided, write the structure of the female reproductive system described.

SKILL: Vocabulary Development

_____ **1.** channel through which a baby passes during childbirth

_____ **2.** also known as the uterine tube

_____ **3.** structure in which a fertilized egg develops

_____ **4.** external structures of the female reproductive system

_____ **5.** structure in which eggs mature

_____ **6.** lower entrance to the uterus

_____ **7.** structure that covers and protects opening to female reproductive system

_____ **8.** structure that controls the opening to the uterus

continued on the next page . . .

Observe the figure below and insert the correct label on the lines provided.

SKILL: **Interpreting Graphics**

9. The diagram below shows the structure of the female reproductive system. Write the following labels on the diagram: "Cervix," "Fallopian tube," "Labia," "Ovary," "Uterus," and "Vagina." Write your answers on the lines provided.

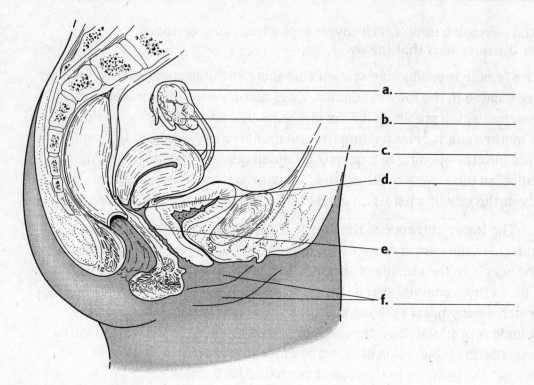

a. _____

b. _____

c. _____

d. _____

e. _____

f. _____

Read the question and write your answer in the space provided.

SKILL: **Vocabulary Development**

10. What is the meaning of the term *collectively* in the passage?

_____

_____

Circle the letter of the word or phrase that best completes the analogy.

11. Vulva is to labia as uterus is to

   a. ovary.

   b. egg.

   c. fallopian tube.

   d. cervix.

CHAPTER 51 ACTIVE READING WORKSHEETS

REPRODUCTIVE SYSTEM

Section 51-3: Gestation

Read the passage below, which covers topics from your textbook. Answer the questions that follow.

Immediately following fertilization and while still in the fallopian tube, the zygote begins a series of mitotic divisions known as *cleavage*. The resulting cells do not increase in size during these cell divisions. Cleavage produces a ball of cells called a *morula*, which is not much larger than the zygote. Cells of the morula divide and release a fluid, resulting in a blastocyst. A **blastocyst** is a ball of cells with a large, fluid-filled cavity.

By the time it reaches the uterus, the morula has become a blastocyst. In the uterus, the blastocyst attaches to the thickened uterine lining. The blastocyst then releases an enzyme that breaks down the epithelial tissue that lines the uterus and burrows into the thickened lining. The process in which the blastocyst burrows and embeds itself into the lining of the uterus is called **implantation,** which occurs about a week after fertilization.

Fill in the blank to complete each sentence.

SKILL: Completing Sentences

1. While still in the fallopian tube, a zygote begins a series of mitotic divisions known as _____

   _____.

2. Cleavage produces a ball of cells called a _____.

3. By the time the morula has reached the uterus, the morula has become a _____.

4. The process in which a blastocyst burrows and embeds itself into the lining of the uterus is called

   _____.

5. Pregnancy begins at implantation, which occurs about a week after _____.

Circle the letter of the word that best completes the analogy.

6. Fertilization is to zygote as cleavage is to

   a. implantation.   **c.** morula.

   b. blastocyst.   **d.** Both (a) and (b)

Answer Key

•••

CHAPTER 1
The Science of Life

SECTION 1-1: THE WORLD OF BIOLOGY

1. All living things and many nonliving things grow.
2. *Uninucleate* means "having one nucleus," while *multinucleate* means "having more than two nuclei."
3. d

SECTION 1-2: THEMES IN BIOLOGY

1. Sentence 1
2. They give three examples of the diversity of life.
3. Sentence 5
4. b

SECTION 1-3: THE STUDY OF BIOLOGY

1. hypothesis, prediction, experiment
2. A hypothesis is a statement that explains observations and data that can be tested. A prediction is a statement made in advance that states the results from testing a true hypothesis. An experiment is a process of testing a hypothesis and its predictions by gathering data under controlled conditions.
3. c
4. b
5. a
6. b
7. c
8. b
9. a
10. b
11. a. 3
    b. 4
    c. 1
    d. 5
    e. 2
12. d

SECTION 1-4: TOOLS AND TECHNIQUES

1. SI Base Units
2. seven rows and three columns
3. name of SI base unit to its abbreviation
4. base quantity to name of SI unit
5. the chemistry of heat
6. c

CHAPTER 2
Chemistry of Life

SECTION 2-1: COMPOSITION OF MATTER

1. P
2. E
3. N
4. P, N
5. P
6. a

SECTION 2-2: ENERGY

1. a redox reaction in which a reactant loses one or more electrons and becomes positive in charge
2. a redox reaction in which a reactant gains one or more electrons and becomes negative in charge
3. b

SECTION 2-3: WATER AND SOLUTIONS

1. Sentence 1
2. Substances that form solutions can be in any state of matter.
3. d

CHAPTER 3
Biochemistry

SECTION 3-1: CARBON COMPOUNDS

1. the hydroxyl group attached to one of its carbon atoms
2. It can cause blindness and/or death.
3. a substance having or containing water
4. c

SECTION 3-2: MOLECULES OF LIFE

1. structure
2. triglycerides, phospholipids, and waxes
3. saturated fatty acids
4. soft or liquid
5. lipid bilayer
6. water
7. stable and effective barrier
8. plants
9. W
10. T
11. P
12. P
13. T
14. W
15. The substance has a fatty appearance.
16. a

CHAPTER 4
Cell Structure and Function

SECTION 4-1: THE HISTORY OF CELL BIOLOGY
1. the invention of the microscope
2. cells
3. the remains of dead plant cells
4. He was the first person to observe living cells.
5. All living things are composed of one or more cells, cells are the basic unit of structure and function in an organism, and cells come only from the reproduction of existing cells.
6. **a.** Robert Hooke
   b. 1673
   c. observed living cells
   d. stated that all plants are made of cells
   e. 1839
   f. Theodor Schwann
   g. Rudolf Virchow
   h. stated that cells come from other cells
7. b

SECTION 4-2: INTRODUCTION TO CELLS
1. organs
2. whole to part
3. d

SECTION 4-3: CELL ORGANELLES AND FEATURES
1. Both are types of outer boundaries through which substances pass.
2. Both are structures that are in the central core of another structure.
3. d

SECTION 4-4: UNIQUE FEATURES OF PLANT CELLS
1. It absorbs light energy to make carbohydrates from carbon dioxide and water.
2. Chloroplasts are believed to have evolved when ancient prokaryotic cells were incorporated into plant cells through a process called endosymbiosis.

CHAPTER 5
Homeostasis and Cell Transport

SECTION 5-1: PASSIVE TRANSPORT
1. **a.** 5
   b. 2
   c. 4
   d. 1
   e. 6
   f. 3
2. **a.** A carrier protein binds to a molecule on one side of the cell membrane.
   b. The carrier protein changes shape, shielding the molecule from the interior of the membrane.
   c. The molecule is released on the other side of the membrane, and the carrier protein returns to its original shape.

3. Through diffusion, molecules move from an area of higher concentration into an area of lower concentration, where they spread apart.
4. d

SECTION 5-2: ACTIVE TRANSPORT
1. macromolecules
2. vesicle
3. proteins, waste products, or toxins
4. c

CHAPTER 6
Photosynthesis

SECTION 6-1: THE LIGHT REACTIONS
1. Sentence 1
2. that there are several different types of chlorophyll, the most common of which are chlorophyll *a* and chlorophyll *b*
3. A slight difference in molecular structure causes the two molecules to absorb different colors of light.
4. a difference
5. that chlorophyll *a* absorbs less blue light but more red light than chlorophyll *b* does
6. a similarity
7. that neither chlorophyll *a* nor chlorophyll *b* absorbs much green light.
8. a larger spectrum of light can be absorbed
9. b

SECTION 6-2: THE CALVIN CYCLE
1. **a.** CO_2 combines with RuBP to form two molecules of 3-PGA.
   b. Each molecule of 3-PGA is converted into a molecule of G3P.
   c. One molecule of G3P is used to make organic compounds.
   d. Most of the G3P is converted back into RuBP.
2. Identifying the word parts that form the word *cytology* and knowing their meanings indicate that cytology is the branch of science that deals with the study of cells.
3. d

CHAPTER 7
Cellular Respiration

SECTION 7-1: GLYCOLYSIS AND FERMENTATION
1. sequencing information
2. two three-carbon molecules of pyruvic acid
3. **a.** Glucose
   b. 2 ATP
   c. 6 carbon compound
   d. 2 molecules of G3P
   e. 2 molecules of three-carbon compound
   f. 4 ATP
   g. 2 molecules of pyruvic acid
4. d

SECTION 7-2: AEROBIC RESPIRATION

1. **a.** 2
   b. 5
   c. 3
   d. 1
   e. 4
2. **a.** citric acid
   b. 5-carbon compound
   c. 4-carbon compound
   d. 4-carbon compound
   e. oxaloacetic acid
3. b

CHAPTER 8
Cell Reproduction

SECTION 8-1: CHROMOSOMES

1. Both males and females have two sex chromosomes, one of which is an X chromosome. The second sex chromosome differs between males and females. Males have a Y chromosome and females have a second X chromosome.
2. Homologues are copies of an autosome, are the same size as one another, and carry genes for the same traits.
3. c

SECTION 8-2: CELL DIVISION

1. c
2. a
3. d
4. b
5. a
6. d
7. c
8. a
9. d
10. **a.** Centrosome
    b. Centromere
    c. Spindle fibers
    d. Nuclear envelope
11. Prophase
12. Metaphase
13. Anaphase
14. Telophase
15. b

SECTION 8-3: MEIOSIS

1. Sperm and egg cells each contain 23 chromosomes.
2. The fusion of sperm and egg results in a zygote.
3. Portions of the chromatids may break off and attach to adjacent chromatids on the homologous chromosome.
4. Through crossing-over, genetic material is exchanged between maternal and paternal chromosomes.

5. Through synapsis, chromatids on homologous chromosomes may come in contact with one another and exchange genetic material.
6. d

CHAPTER 9
Fundamentals of Genetics

SECTION 9-1: MENDEL'S LEGACY

1. separate
2. one factor from each pair
3. fertilization
4. a pair of factors is segregated, or separated, during the formation of gametes
5. together
6. b

SECTION 9-2: GENETIC CROSSES

1. **a.** to show the probability that certain traits will be inherited by offspring
   b. Each parent has one dominant allele (*B*) and one recessive allele (*b*) for coat color.
   c. Because each parent has one dominant allele, both parents have black coat color.
   d. Two homozygous offspring are predicted, one with the genotype *BB* and one with the genotype *bb*.
   e. 1 *BB*: 2 *Bb*: 1 *bb*
   f. 3 black: 1 brown
2. Phenotype refers to the appearance of an organism as a result of its genotype, or how the traits show in the organism.
3. d

CHAPTER 10
DNA, RNA, and Protein Synthesis

SECTION 10-1: DISCOVERY OF DNA

1. protease
2. DNase
3. The batch containing heat-killed *S* cells, DNase, and live *R* cells resulted in the mice surviving.
4. b

SECTION 10-2: DNA STRUCTURE

1. Sentence 2
2. DNA is made up of repeating subunits called nucleotides.
3. It explains that each DNA molecule contains two chains of nucleotides.
4. d

SECTION 10-3: DNA REPLICATION

1. DNA polymerases add new complementary nucleotides, found floating freely inside the nucleus, to the original strands of DNA.
2. Helicases move along the DNA molecule, separating the two strands by breaking the hydrogen bonds between complementary nitrogenous bases.
3. a

SECTION 10-4: PROTEIN SYNTHESIS

1. Each codon codes for a specific amino acid sequence, which results in the production of a protein, or protein synthesis.
2. the presence of the start codon, AUG
3. the presence of a stop codon, such as UAA, UAG, or UGA
4. a

CHAPTER 11
Gene Expression

SECTION 11-1: CONTROL OF GENE EXPRESSION

1. DNA and histones are tightly coiled prior to mitosis and meiosis. These coils relax after mitosis or meiosis has occurred.
2. The promoter is the binding site in both types of cells.
3. b

SECTION 11-2: GENE EXPRESSION IN DEVELOPMENT AND CELL DIVISION

1. sarcoma
2. body part to type of malignant tumor that grows in that location
3. c

CHAPTER 12
Inheritance Patterns and Human Genetics

SECTION 12-1: CHROMOSOMES AND INHERITANCE

1. substitution
2. mutate, mutant, mutagen, mutative
3. d

SECTION 12-2: HUMAN GENETICS

1. inability to distinguish certain colors, particularly red and green
2. Hemophilia
3. muscle tissue is progressively weakened and destroyed
4. b

CHAPTER 13
Gene Technology

SECTION 13-1: DNA TECHNOLOGY

1. a. 2
   b. 5
   c. 3
   d. 1
   e. 6
   f. 4
2. a. Bacterium
   b. Plasmid
   c. Donor gene

3. The plasmid is cut with a restriction enzyme.
4. The donor gene is inserted into the plasmid.
5. The plasmid containing the donor gene is inserted into the bacterium.
6. As the bacterium divides, the plasmid replicates and clones the donor gene.
7. to separate or set apart
8. b

SECTION 13-2: THE HUMAN GENOME PROJECT

1. sentence 1
2. sentence 5
3. Sentence 2 defines the term *proteomics*.
4. sentence 4
5. *Abundances* means how much of each protein is found in an organism.
6. b

SECTION 13-3: GENETIC ENGINEERING

1. influenza, smallpox, and polio
2. vaccines
3. virus or a bacterium
4. pathogen
5. cause disease
6. pathogen's surface proteins
7. it is intended to protect against
8. genetic engineering
9. harmless virus
10. genome of a pathogen
11. unaltered forms of the pathogen
12. to avert or keep from happening
13. d

CHAPTER 14
History of Life

SECTION 14-1: BIOGENESIS

1. boiled broth
2. After the curved neck is removed, the broth becomes cloudy and contaminated with organisms.
3. b

SECTION 14-2: EARTH'S HISTORY

1. a method of establishing the age of materials
2. an unstable nucleus
3. the length of time one-half of a radioactive isotope takes to decay
4. d

SECTION 14-3: THE FIRST LIFE-FORMS

1. If the environment contains a fixed number of nucleotides, then competition would occur among similar RNA molecules.
2. Because of replication, a parent RNA molecule may pass on to its offspring any advantages it possesses for obtaining nucleotides from the environment.
3. d

CHAPTER 15
Theory of Evolution

SECTION 15-1: HISTORY OF EVOLUTIONARY THOUGHT

1. Descent with modification states that every species—living or extinct—has descended by reproduction from preexisting species and must be able to change over time.
2. The finches on the Galápagos Islands with different beaks adapted for different kinds of food. Darwin believed all the finches had descended from a few ancestral finches.
3. b

SECTION 15-2: EVIDENCE OF EVOLUTION

1. microscope
2. plants and animals
3. the same age
4. a

SECTION 15-3: EVOLUTION IN ACTION

1. Coevolution
2. Divergent evolution
3. a change in two or more species in close association with each other
4. when unrelated species become more similar as they adapt to the same kind of environment
5. shark and porpoise
6. two breeds of dogs
7. c

CHAPTER 16
Population Genetics and Speciation

SECTION 16-1: GENETIC EQUILIBRIUM

1. The phenotype frequency of the first generation is 0.5 pink, 0.5 red, and 0.0 white. The phenotype frequency of the second generation is 0.25 pink, 0.63 red, and 0.13 white.
2. The allele frequency of both the first and second generation is $0.75R$ and $0.25r$.
3. b

SECTION 16-2: DISRUPTION OF GENETIC EQUILIBRIUM

1. Sentence 1
2. One requirement of genetic equilibrium is the presence of a large population.
3. a

SECTION 16-3: FORMATION OF SPECIES

1. term to definition
2. postzygotic isolation
3. c

CHAPTER 17
Classification of Organisms

SECTION 17-1: BIODIVERSITY

1. phylum
2. species identifier
3. b

SECTION 17-2: SYSTEMATICS

1. Cladistics is a system of phylogenetic classification that uses shared derived characters to establish evolutionary relationships.
2. feathers
3. c

SECTION 17-3: MODERN CLASSIFICATION

1. Archaea and Bacteria
2. Members of the kingdom Fungi may be unicellular or multicellular while members of the kingdom Animalia are all multicellular.
3. d

CHAPTER 18
Introduction to Ecology

SECTION 18-1: INTRODUCTION TO ECOLOGY

1. to make carbohydrates
2. The main topic is the interdependence of all organisms on other organisms and the nonliving portion of the environment.
3. d

SECTION 18-2: ECOLOGY OF ORGANISMS

1. Both biotic factors and abiotic factors are components of an environment that influences an organism; both types of factors are not independent. Biotic factors are all living organisms in an environment, and abiotic factors are nonliving factors in an environment.
2. In the passage, the term refers to agents that affect a situation or process. In mathematics class, the term refers to values that produce a product.
3. b

SECTION 18-3: ENERGY TRANSFER

1. photosynthesis and chemosynthesis
2. Producers are autotrophs that capture energy and use it to make organic compounds. Cosumers are heterotrophs that obtain energy by consuming organic molecules made by other organisms.
3. d

SECTION 18-4: ECOSYSTEM RECYCLING

1. **a.** 3
   b. 4
   c. 1
   d. 2
2. nitrification
3. anaerobic bacteria

4. nitrogen gas
5. nitrogen-fixing bacteria
6. ecosystem
7. Ammonification is the act of releasing ammonia compounds.
8. d

CHAPTER 19
Populations

SECTION 19-1: UNDERSTANDING POPULATIONS

1. **a.** random distribution
   b. clumped distribution
   c. even distribution
2. uniform or conforming to the same principles
3. a

SECTION 19-2: MEASURING POPULATIONS

1. Both models describe the influence that birthrates and death rates have on population size. In the exponential model, it is assumed that birthrates and death rates remain constant and that the larger the population gets, the faster it grows. In the logistic model, it is assumed that birthrates decline and death rates rise with population size due to limiting factors.
2. to limit or restrict
3. c

SECTION 19-3: HUMAN POPULATION GROWTH

1. developing countries
2. developed country
3. 0.003 per capita
4. exceed its birth rates
5. 0.015 per capita
6. a

CHAPTER 20
Community Ecology

SECTION 20-1: SPECIES INTERACTIONS

1. similarities and differences
2. In the passage, the term *derive* means "to obtain or receive."
3. a

SECTION 20-2: PATTERNS IN COMMUNITIES

1. identifying main ideas
2. species extinction
3. c
4. primary succession
5. farming
6. their seeds
7. d

CHAPTER 21
Ecosystems

SECTION 21-1: TERRESTRIAL BIOMES

1. tundras and deserts
2. savanna
3. c

SECTION 21-2: AQUATIC ECOSYSTEMS

1. about 70 percent
2. intertidal zone, neritic zone, oceanic zone
3. The oceanic zone lies beyond the continental shelf.
4. Both zones are subdivisions of the oceanic zone. The pelagic zone is the open ocean, while the benthic zone is the ocean bottom.
5. **a.** Oceanic zone
   b. Neritic zone
   c. Intertidal zone
   d. Pelagic zone
   e. Aphotic zone
   f. Benthic zone
6. factor or trait that is not constant
7. c

CHAPTER 22
Humans and the Environment

SECTION 22-1: AN INTERCONNECTED PLANET

1. Answers include: provide food, fuel, medicines, and useful chemicals, and recycle wastes.
2. biologist, E.O. Wilson
3. d

SECTION 22-2: ENVIRONMENTAL ISSUES

1. The thinning areas in the ozone layer may result in an increase in human skin cancer and also disrupt ecosystems by harming plants and photosynthetic algae.
2. In the passage, the term *depletion* means "to decrease or lessen quantity."
3. c

SECTION 22-3: ENVIRONMENTAL SOLUTIONS

1. As the human population has increased, natural resources have been destroyed. The distruction of natural resources has brought about losses in biodiversity.
2. field of study
3. b

CHAPTER 23
Bacteria

SECTION 23-1: PROKARYOTES

1. thermoacidophiles
2. c

SECTION 23-2: BIOLOGY OF PROKARYOTES

1. cytoplasm or chromosome
2. endospore
3. d

SECTION 23-3: BACTERIA AND HUMANS

1. Bacteria cause disease in several ways.
2. A pathogen is a substance that causes disease, which, in turn, causes suffering in the individuals the pathogen affects.
3. a

CHAPTER 24
Viruses

SECTION 24-1: VIRAL STRUCTURE AND REPLICATION

1. **a.** Nucleic acid
   b. Head
   c. Collar
   d. Sheath
   e. Tail
   f. Base plate
   g. Tail fibers
2. b

SECTION 24-2: VIRAL DISEASES

1. synthesis
2. immune system
3. host system
4. d

CHAPTER 25
Protists

SECTION 25-1: CHARACTERISTICS OF PROTISTS

1. amoebas
2. euglenoids
3. colony
4. multicellular
5. Red algae
6. a

SECTION 25-2: ANIMAL-LIKE PROTISTS

1. Members of all phyla of animal-like protists are either heterotrophic or parasitic.
2. ciliates
3. c

SECTION 25-3: PLANTLIKE AND FUNGUSLIKE PROTISTS

1. They have chlorophyll and are photosynthetic.
2. They lack a cell wall and are highly motile.
3. b

SECTION 25-4: PROTISTS AND HUMANS

1. *Anopheles* mosquito
2. spaces between events
3. a

CHAPTER 26
Fungi

SECTION 26-1: OVERVIEW OF FUNGI

1. Both are examples of fungi.
2. as an animal or fungus
3. d

SECTION 26-2: CLASSIFICATION OF FUNGI

1. a symbiotic association between a fungus and plant roots
2. a symbiotic relationship between a fungus and a photosynthetic partner
3. c

SECTION 26-3: FUNGI AND HUMANS

1. mushrooms, truffles, and morels
2. vitamins, minerals, and other nutrients
3. grain or fruit
4. a

CHAPTER 27
The Importance of Plants

SECTION 27-1: PLANTS AND PEOPLE

1. root crops
2. vegetables
3. cereals
4. legumes
5. b

SECTION 27-2: PLANTS AND THE ENVIRONMENT

1. The study of the interaction between plants and the environment is called plant ecology.
2. The sentence explains how organic compounds from plants benefit consumers.
3. necessary or indispensable
4. d

CHAPTER 28
Plant Evolution and Classification

SECTION 28-1: OVERVIEW OF PLANTS

1. ferns
2. gymnosperm
3. a

SECTION 28-2: NONVASCULAR PLANTS

1. They lack vascular tissue.
2. A new layer of soil is created.
3. b

SECTION 28-3: VASCULAR PLANTS

1. Both types of leaves possess venation. In a monocot leaf, the venation is parallel. A dicot leaf has net venation.
2. Both types of stems contain vascular bundles. A monocot stem has scattered bundles, while a dicot stem has radially arranged vascular bundles.
3. d

CHAPTER 29
Plant Structure and Function

SECTION 29-1: PLANT CELLS AND TISSUES

1. diameter
2. cork cambium
3. a

SECTION 29-2: ROOTS

1. moves easily through the soil as it grows
2. ability to absorb water and mineral nutrients
3. slippery
4. c

SECTION 29-3: STEMS

1. translocation
2. a positive pressure build-up
3. In the passage, *source* refers to a place where sugars are made in the plant. In the reference section of a research paper, the term refers to a document that supplies primary information.
4. a. Phloem
   b. Source
   c. Sink
   d. Sugar
   e. Water
5. d

SECTION 29-4: LEAVES

1. not able to penetrate; steadfast
2. epidermis
3. petiole
4. spongy mesophyll
5. blade
6. mesophyll
7. simple leaf
8. palisade mesophyll
9. compound leaves
10. a. Cuticle
    b. Upper epidermis
    c. Palisade mesophyll
    d. Spongy mesophyll
11. b

CHAPTER 30
Plant Reproduction

SECTION 30-1: PLANT LIFE CYCLES

1. In the passage, the term refers to overlapping external structures of a cone. In a music class, the term refers to a series of tones produced at regular intervals.
2. a. Microsporangium
   b. Meiosis
   c. Pollen grain
   d. Ovule
   e. Micropyle
   f. Pollen tube
   g. Fertilization
   h. Seed
   i. Megasporangium
3. c

SECTION 30-2: SEXUAL REPRODUCTION IN FLOWERING PLANTS

1. ovary
2. sepals
3. stigma
4. carpels
5. anther
6. stamens
7. a. Stamen
   b. Filament
   c. Anther
   d. Stigma
   e. Style
   f. Ovary
   g. Pistil
   h. Petal
   i. Sepal
   j. Ovule
8. having a common center
9. a

SECTION 30-3: DISPERSAL AND PROPAGATION

1. a. Hypocotyl
   b. Plumule
   c. Radicle
   d. Cotyledon
   e. Seed coat
2. Both types of seeds are plant embryos surrounded by a seed coat. They differ in that a bean seed is a dicot while a corn kernel is a monocot. They also differ in the functions of their cotyledons.
3. The endosperm was absorbed by the fleshy cotyledons.
4. The hilum marks the place where the seed was attached to the ovary wall.
5. The cotyledon absorbs nutrients from the endosperm and transfers them to the embryo.
6. curved inward
7. d

CHAPTER 31
Plant Responses

SECTION 31-1: PLANT HORMONES

1. Plant hormones are chemical messengers that affect a plant's ability to respond to its environment.

2. auxins, gibberellins, ethylene, cytokinins, and abscisic acid

3. a

SECTION 31-2: PLANT MOVEMENTS

1. thigmotropism

2. gravity

3. Answers will vary but may include: photosynthesis, photoreceptor, photoautotroph, and photoperiodism.

4. c

SECTION 31-3: SEASONAL RESPONSES

1. a cause-and-effect text structure

2. Some tree leaves change colors in the fall due to a photoperiodic response and temperature change.

3. to decompose

4. c

CHAPTER 32
Introduction to Animals

SECTION 32-1: THE NATURE OF ANIMALS

1. recognizing similarities and differences

2. A sponge lacks symmetry, while a jellyfish possesses radial symmetry.

3. Both radial and bilateral symmetry are consistent overall patterns of structure. The traits differ in the particular pattern. Radial symmetry refers to a pattern in which similar parts branch out from a central axis. Bilateral symmetry refers to two similar halves on either side of a central plane.

4. a. no symmetry
   b. radial symmetry
   c. bilateral symmetry

5. d

SECTION 32-2: INVERTEBRATES AND VERTEBRATES

1. oxygen and nutrients

2. carbon dioxide and wastes

3. diffusion across cell membranes

4. open circulatory system

5. c

SECTION 32-3: FERTILIZATION AND DEVELOPMENT

1. development of germ layers into certain body organs

2. mesoderm

3. mesoderm

4. ectoderm

5. endoderm

6. a. blastula
   b. gastrula
   c. endoderm
   d. mesoderm

7. c

CHAPTER 33
Sponges, Cnidarians, and Ctenophores

SECTION 33-1: PORIFERA

1. The body plan of a sponge suggests a relationship between structure and function.

2. two cell layers separated by a jellylike substance

3. As the choanocytes lining the interior cylinder of a sponge beat their flagella, water is drawn through ostia in the body wall and moves into the hollow cylinder. The water then exits through the osculum.

4. a. Choanocyte
   b. Flagellum
   c. Osculum
   d. Ostium
   e. Spicules
   f. Interior of sponge

5. c

SECTION 33-2: CNIDARIA AND CTENOPHORA

1. All cnidarians have a body made up of two cell layers.

2. Due to its vase-shaped form, a polyp is sessile. The bell-shaped body of the medusa, however, is specialized for swimming.

3. Cnidarians have an outer epidermis, inner gastrodermis, jellylike mesoglea, a gastrovascular cavity, a mouth, and tentacles.

4. a. Medusa
   b. Polyp
   c. Epidermis
   d. Mesoglea
   e. Gastrovascular cavity
   f. Gastrodermis
   g. Tentacle
   h. Mouth

5. not free moving; fixed

6. a

CHAPTER 34
Flatworms, Roundworms, and Rotifers

SECTION 34-1: PLATYHELMINTHES

1. a. 7
   b. 3
   c. 9
   d. 5
   e. 2
   f. 8
   g. 4
   h. 6
   i. 1

2. a. Primary host
   b. Eggs

c. Egg
d. Ciliated larvae
e. Intermediate host
f. Tailed larva
3. having cilia
4. c

SECTION 34-2: NEMATODA AND ROTIFERA

1. a circle around the head region
2. The mastax breaks food into smaller pieces.
3. a. Cilia
   b. Mouth
   c. Eyespot
   d. Flame cells
   e. Excretory tubule
   f. Stomach
   g. Intestine
   h. Anus
   i. Cerebral ganglion
   j. Mastax
   k. Ovary
   l. Cloaca
4. The mastax is a muscular organ that breaks food down into small particles.
5. digestive, reproductive, and excretory systems
6. Both rotifers and planarians use flame cells and excretory tubules to collect excess water in the body.
7. c

CHAPTER 35
Mollusks and Annelids

SECTION 35-1: MOLLUSCA

1. Bivalves possess two external shells, most gastropods have one shell, and most cephalopods have no shell.
2. a head and radula
3. the ability to move from place to place
4. b

SECTION 35-2: ANNELIDA

1. Segmentation aids in the locomotion of the earthworm.
2. The earthworm's body is divided into more than 100 identical segments, and circular and longitudinal muscles line the animal's interior body wall.
3. d

CHAPTER 36
Arthropods

SECTION 36-1: PHYLUM ARTHROPODA

1. The tissues of an arthropod swell until they put a good deal of pressure on the exoskeleton.
2. The cells of the epidermis secrete enzymes that digest the inner layer of the exoskeleton, and the epidermis begins to synthesize a new exoskeleton.
3. c

SECTION 36-2: SUBPHYLUM CRUSTACEA

1. cheliped
2. maxilliped
3. b

SECTION 36-3: SUBPHYLA CHELICERATA AND MYRIAPODA

1. gas exchange
2. tracheae
3. Malpighian tubules
4. c

CHAPTER 37
Insects

SECTION 37-1: THE INSECT WORLD

1. forewings
2. mesothorax
3. exoskeleton
4. b

SECTION 37-2: INSECT BEHAVIOR

1. An innate behavior is genetically determined rather than learned.
2. worker bees, queen bees, and drones
3. a

CHAPTER 38
Echinoderms and Invertebrate Chordates

SECTION 38-1: ECHINODERMS

1. a. 3
   b. 8
   c. 1
   d. 6
   e. 4
   f. 2
   g. 7
   h. 5
2. a sievelike plate on the aboral surface of an echinoderm
3. Valves prevent the backward flow of water.
4. Muscles lining the tube feet have contracted, forcing water back into the ampullae and shortening the tube feet.
5. In the passage, the term *feet* refers to a body part used for movement, while in the sentence, the term refers to a unit of measure equal to 12 inches.
6. b

SECTION 38-2: INVERTEBRATE CHORDATES

1. similarities and differences
2. Sentence 5 describes the location of the pharyngeal pouches.

3. Sentences 6 and 7 describe the differences in structures that have evolved from the common pharyngeal pouches.
4. Both structures evolved from pharyngeal pouches.
5. a. Dorsal nerve cord
   b. Notochord
   c. Pharyngeal pouch
   d. Postanal tail
6. pierced or punched with holes
7. c

CHAPTER 39
Fishes

SECTION 39-1: INTRODUCTION TO VERTEBRATES
1. Vertebrates have the same characteristics as other chordates, but also have unique characteristics.
2. vertebrae, bones, or cartilage that protect the dorsal nerve cord; a cranium or skull that protects the brain; an endoskeleton composed of bone or cartilage
3. cranium or skull
4. d

SECTION 39-2: JAWLESS AND CARTILAGINOUS FISHES
1. Sentence 1 contrasts fertilization in cartilaginous and jawless fishes.
2. The sentence identifies a similarity: all cartilaginous fishes do not care for their young after birth or hatching.
3. c

SECTION 39-3: BONY FISHES
1. a. Blood flow from the body
   b. Atrium
   c. Sinus venosus
   d. Ventricle
   e. Conus arteriosus
   f. Blood flow to the gills
2. a. 2
   b. 6
   c. 4
   d. 1
   e. 5
   f. 3
3. an enclosed space or compartment; cavity
4. a

CHAPTER 40
Amphibians

SECTION 40-1: ORIGIN AND EVOLUTION OF AMPHIBIANS
1. similarities and differences
2. All early amphibians had four strong limbs.
3. They are homologous to the pectoral fins of fishes.
4. b

SECTION 40-2: CHARACTERISTICS OF AMPHIBIANS
1. vent
2. small intestine
3. stomach
4. large intestine
5. mesentery
6. cloaca
7. a. Esophagus
   b. Mouth
   c. Small intestine
   d. Ileum
   e. Large intestine
   f. Cloaca
   g. Vent
   h. Stomach
   i. Duodenum
   j. Pyloric sphincter
   k. Mesentery
8. Something that is indigestible is "not able to be digested."
9. a

SECTION 40-3: REPRODUCTION IN AMPHIBIANS
1. Parental care is common among amphibians.
2. to prevent the eggs from desiccating
3. b

CHAPTER 41
Reptiles

SECTION 41-1: ORIGIN AND EVOLUTION OF REPTILES
1. cause of the extinction of dinosaurs
2. The dust particles in the atmosphere would block sunlight from reaching Earth's surface.
3. c

SECTION 41-2: CHARACTERISTICS OF REPTILES
1. The patterns differ in how long the eggs remain within the female and in how she provides them with nutrition.
2. An egg produced through oviparity is enclosed in a tough shell, while an egg produced through viviparity lacks such a shell.
3. a placenta
4. ovoviviparity and viviparity
5. ovoviviparity
6. viviparity
7. oviparity
8. ovoviviparity
9. oviparity
10. viviparity
11. An item that is retained is kept in its original position, or "held back."
12. b

SECTION 41-3: MODERN REPTILES

1. Squamata
2. an upper jaw loosely joined to the skull
3. agility, speed, and camouflage
4. a

CHAPTER 42
Birds

SECTION 42-1: ORIGIN AND EVOLUTION OF BIRDS

1. anatomy, physiology, and behavior
2. wings
3. terrestrial
4. leapt after prey
5. c

SECTION 42-2: CHARACTERISTICS OF BIRDS

1. **a.** 5
   b. 3
   c. 1
   d. 4
   e. 2
2. Posterior refers to an item that is located behind something. The posterior air sacs are located behind, or posterior to, the lungs.
3. a

SECTION 42-3: CLASSIFICATION

1. swift
2. walking and running
3. to entrap or catch
4. c

CHAPTER 43
Mammals

SECTION 43-1: ORIGIN AND EVOLUTION OF MAMMALS

1. A major evolutionary split occurred in the terrestrial vertebrates, which produced two groups of animals.
2. The outer layer of a synapsid's skull has a single opening behind the eye socket.
3. b

SECTION 43-2: CHARACTERISTICS OF MAMMALS

1. cellulose
2. enzymes
3. microorganisms
4. stomach
5. rumen
6. molecules
7. small intestine
8. cecum
9. small intestine
10. fermentation chamber
11. stomach
12. to pass from the stomach into the mouth
13. b

SECTION 43-3: DIVERSITY OF MAMMALS

1. Members of order Dermoptera can glide through the air, a trait members of the other orders lack.
2. an organism that feeds on insects
3. a

SECTION 43-4: PRIMATES AND HUMAN ORIGINS

1. Anthropoids have characteristic adaptations.
2. Anthropoid adaptations include rotating shoulder and elbow joints; opposable thumbs; two incisors, one canine, two premolars, three molars on each half of the upper and lower mouth; complex brain structure and large brain size relative to body size.
3. c

CHAPTER 44
Animal Behavior

SECTION 44-1: DEVELOPMENT OF BEHAVIOR

1. genes
2. environmental
3. diseased young
4. ignore
5. removing diseased young to keep the hive clean and disease-free

SECTION 44-2: TYPES OF ANIMAL BEHAVIOR

1. Certain criteria must be met for communication to be considered language.
2. The criteria include phonemes, productivity, and grammar.
3. b

CHAPTER 45
Skeletal, Muscular, and Integumentary Systems

SECTION 45-1: THE HUMAN BODY PLAN

1. The immune system is an organ system that works to keep the body exempt from the actions of pathogens and/or exempt from disease.
2. structure to organ system it belongs to
3. protection
4. organ system to function
5. c
6. respiratory and excretory systems
7. circulatory and immune systems
8. endocrine and reproductive systems

SECTION 45-2: SKELETAL SYSTEM

1. Semimovable joints allow limited—or partial—movement.

2. saddle joint
3. hinge joint
4. gliding joint
5. fixed joint
6. ball-and-socket joint
7. b

SECTION 45-3: MUSCULAR SYSTEM
1. Bones move when muscles pull on them.
2. The arm bends at the elbow.
3. The arm straightens.
4. a

SECTION 45-4: INTEGUMENTARY SYSTEM
1. similarities and differences
2. Both are exocrine glands that release secretions through ducts. The main difference lies in the type of substance secreted. Sweat glands release excess water, salts, and urea. Oil glands secrete the fatty substance sebum.
3. d

CHAPTER 46
Circulatory and Respiratory Systems

SECTION 46-1: THE CIRCULATORY SYSTEM
1. coronary and renal hepatic portal, circulation
2. They differ in the particular area of the body to which they move blood. Coronary circulation supplies blood to the heart. Renal circulation supplies blood to the kidneys. Hepatic portal circulation supplies blood to the liver.
3. Renal circulation supplies blood to the kidneys.
4. c

SECTION 46-2: BLOOD
1. a. 5
   b. 2
   c. 6
   d. 1
   e. 3
   f. 4
2. c

SECTION 46-3: THE RESPIRATORY SYSTEM
1. consisting of cartilage
2. larynx
3. alveoli
4. pharynx
5. epiglottis
6. bronchi
7. a. Pharynx
   b. Epiglottis
   c. Larynx
   d. Trachea
   e. Lung
   f. Bronchus
   g. Bronchiole
   h. Alveoli
8. d

CHAPTER 47
The Body's Defense Systems

SECTION 47-1: NONSPECIFIC DEFENSES
1. a pathogen that penetrates the skin or a mucous membrane
2. damage to a blood cell
3. d

SECTION 47-2: SPECIFIC DEFENSES: THE IMMUNE SYSTEM
1. A person who is resistant to a specific pathogen is said to have an immunity to it.
2. polio, measles, mumps, tetanus, and diphtheria
3. b

SECTION 47-3: HIV AND AIDS
1. vaccine
2. resistant
3. a combination of three drugs
4. d

CHAPTER 48
Digestive and Excretory Systems

SECTION 48-1: NUTRIENTS
1. potassium
2. hemoglobin
3. calcium and phosphorous
4. a

SECTION 48-2: DIGESTIVE SYSTEM
1. The liver stores glycogen, makes proteins, breaks down toxic substances, and secretes bile.
2. Bile breaks fat globules into small droplets, which exposes a greater surface area of the fats to the action of digestive enzymes.
3. The gallbladder stores and concentrates bile.
4. a. Liver
   b. Common bile duct
   c. Stomach
   d. Main pancreatic duct
   e. Pancreas
   f. Small intestine
   g. Gallbladder
5. In the passage, *suspended* means "dispersed in a liquid." In the sentence, the term means "disbarment of a privilege."
6. c

SECTION 48-3: URINARY SYSTEM
1. Both processes help the body maintain homeostasis.
2. In reabsorption, substances move into the blood, while in secretion, substances move from the blood.
3. b

CHAPTER 49
Nervous System and Sense Organs

SECTION 49-1: NEURONS AND NERVE IMPULSES
1. A substance that is permeable can be penetrated easily.
2. **a.** 4   **g.** 3
   b. 12   **h.** 11
   c. 2   **i.** 6
   d. 8   **j.** 1
   e. 5   **k.** 7
   f. 9   **l.** 10
3. a

SECTION 49-2: STRUCTURE OF THE NERVOUS SYSTEM
1. Sentence 1: The motor division of the peripheral nervous system is composed of the somatic nervous system and the autonomic nervous system.
2. The sentence explains the functions of the autonomic nervous system.
3. b

SECTION 49-3: SENSORY SYSTEMS
1. tissue damage
2. sense organ
3. b

SECTION 49-4: DRUGS AND THE NERVOUS SYSTEM
1. Alcohol is a depressant and decreases the activity of the central nervous system.
2. decreased blood flow to organs, lowered body temperature, lengthening of reactions time, slowed respiration
3. b

CHAPTER 50
Endocrine System

SECTION 50-1: HORMONES
1. endocrine and exocrine glands
2. Ductless means lacking ducts, or tubes, through which substances can travel to other parts of the body.
3. c

SECTION 50-2: ENDOCRINE GLANDS
1. The gland releases more than one hormone.
2. Both types of hormones regulate secondary sex characteristics. However, estrogen regulates these characteristics in females, while androgens regulate these characteristics in males.
3. Both hormones are secreted by the pancreas, and both monitor glucose levels in the body. Glucagon stimulates the release of glucose, while insulin stimulates the absorption of glucose.
4. adrenal medulla
5. thyroid gland
6. pineal gland

7. adrenal cortex
8. parathyroid gland
9. ovary
10. pancreas
11. thymus gland
12. Various hormones identified in the table incite—or goad on—a particular response by the body.
13. a

CHAPTER 51
Reproductive System

SECTION 51-1: MALE REPRODUCTIVE SYSTEM
1. A mature sperm consists of three regions—a head, a midpiece, and a tail.
2. Enzymes contained in the head region help the sperm penetrate protective layers that surround an egg cell.
3. The midpiece is full of mitochondria that supply the energy needed for the sperm to reach an egg.
4. The tail consists of a single flagellum that propels the sperm.
5. **a.** Tail
   b. Midpiece
   c. Head
   d. Mitochondria
   e. Nucleus
   f. Enzymes
6. having reached full growth or development
7. d

SECTION 51-2: FEMALE REPRODUCTIVE SYSTEM
1. vagina
2. fallopian tube
3. uterus
4. vulva
5. ovaries
6. cervix
7. labia
8. sphincter muscle
9. **a.** Fallopian tube
   b. Ovary
   c. Uterus
   d. Cervix
   e. Vagina
   f. Labia
10. taken as a whole unit
11. d

SECTION 51-3: GESTATION
1. cleavage
2. morula
3. blastocyst
4. implantation
5. fertilization
6. c